BEES

THEIR VISION, CHEMICAL
SENSES, AND LANGUAGE

Karl von Frisch

PROFESSOR OF ZOOLOGY IN
THE UNIVERSITY OF MUNICH

Cornell Paperbacks

Cornell University Press

ITHACA, NEW YORK

PRINTED IN THE UNITED STATES OF AMERICA

BY VAIL-BALLOU PRESS, INC.

Foreword

KARL von FRISCH is known throughout the world to
both biologists and beekeepers for his discoveries of remarkable sensory capacities and behavior patterns in
bees and other lower animals. In this book he reviews
these scientific achievements in a straightforward account that requires for its enjoyment neither technical
background nor undue effort on the part of the reader.
Anyone who has kept a hive of bees has been perplexed
at times by the fickle behavior of his charges. In these
pages many of the puzzling habits of honeybees are
lucidly explained and set into proper perspective as key-
stones of an elaborate social structure whose smooth
functioning has long been the envy of philosophers. So
fundamental are certain of the author's discoveries that
their impact will surely be felt not only in apiculture
and zoology but wherever animal behavior and the
mechanism of sense organs are under serious considera-
tion.

In the course of a distinguished scientific career von
Frisch has carried out thorough and rigorous investiga-

tions of a wide variety of biological problems, including the nature of the pigments in the skins of fish, the color changes of animals, the hearing of fish, the chemical senses of both fish and insects, the vision of insects, and most recently the means of communication employed by bees. His book, *Du und das Leben*, presents elementary biology so agreeably that it has been widely read in Austria and Germany. Born and educated in Vienna, he has been a professor at the universities of Rostock, Breslau, Munich, and Graz. For many years he directed the Zoological Institute at Munich. While his work has been widely known and highly respected by professional scientists for many years, very few of his writings have been available in English.

The book begins with a discussion of the co-operative relationship between bees and flowers whereby insects obtain food and the plants achieve the transport of their pollen. We must face the fact that so much has been written about this subject, and with such a surfeit of melodrama, that most of us tend to link it with romantic poetry or nursery tales. One must make a certain effort to clear one's eyes and give fresh, unbiased attention to this matter of the bees and flowers. But here the effort will be well rewarded, for the reader will find that the scientific facts are more intriguing than any artificial embroidery upon them. The third chapter, in particular, leads us to the surprising conclusion that bees manage to communicate to each other precise information about the location of food. The "language" of bees does not employ words or even sounds, but serves nonetheless to convey complex information, and even seems to involve something analogous to map reading.

In recent decades biologists have grown reluctant to credit any claim that the reactions of lower animals attain a high degree of complexity, or what one might be tempted to call intelligence. They recall cases where what was sincerely believed to be intelligent behavior in animals turned out on thorough study to have a much simpler explanation, which did not require us to ascribe higher mental faculties to creatures with much simpler nervous systems than our own. Hence many may feel skeptical at first concerning the conclusions reached in Chapter III, since their wholehearted acceptance involves a considerable revision of current scientific attitudes. As von Frisch phrased the matter himself on one occasion, "No competent scientist *ought* to believe these things on first hearing."

Von Frisch does not present us with vague or mystical speculations but rather with phenomena which, however astonishing they may be, are nonetheless concrete and readily observed. Now that he has told us what to look for in the seething turmoil of bees creeping over the honeycomb, now that his insight has made order where there seemed to be utter chaos, anyone with a little patience and a hive of bees can test the principal conclusions for himself.

Indeed, independent confirmation has already been accomplished in the United States, in England, and on the continent of Europe. For example, Dr. W. H. Thorpe of Cambridge University writes in *Nature:*

Through the kindness . . . of Professor von Frisch I was able . . . to perform with him and for myself . . . "repeats" of certain of the most crucial experiments. . . . My observations covered all the main phases of the work, and I was able to make my own estimates of the efficiency of the indication of distance and direction of food sources. . . . This memorable experience . . . enabled me to resolve to my own satisfaction some of those doubts and difficulties that come to mind on first reading the work, and convinced me of the soundness of the conclusions as a whole.

I confess without embarrassment that until I performed these simple experiments myself, I too retained a residue of skepticism. But a few weeks' work with an observation beehive and a colony of bees (loaned for the purpose by the Department of Entomology of the New York State College of Agriculture) led me to the same degree of conviction as that which Thorpe reports. While certain details remain unclear, and while much additional work must be done before the dances and the "language" of the bees are fully understood, the important basic facts described in Chapter III appear to be established beyond serious question. We shall now be obliged to readjust our thinking about animal behavior in the light of these findings and the implications that flow from them.

Were these its only merits, this book would clearly be of interest to specialists in several fields of science. But many who heard the lectures on which the book is based feel that it has another important role. While the conclusions are of basic importance to biological science and are truly revolutionary in the special field of animal behavior, the phenomena themselves display an intrinsic simplicity that is characteristic of many classic experiments. Hence they provide for the general reader a rare opportunity to appreciate the mode of thinking and the point of view of the critical investigator. The account is condensed, to be sure, with many laborious intervals and false starts left out; but nonetheless as one reads these pages he can feel a real sense of participation in the search for understanding.

Appreciation of a scientist's mode of thinking requires more than a bare scrutiny of phenomena, hypotheses, experiments, and conclusions. The thought and the word are closely linked together; and for this reason an effort has been made to preserve in the printed page something of the pleasing directness and simplicity so apparent in the original lectures. Those who heard the lectures will recognize this flavor; and I believe that many others, a trifle jaded, perhaps, by the conventional jargon of scientific writing, will be refreshed by the straightforward clarity of this account.

DONALD R. GRIFFIN

Department of Zoology
Cornell University

Preface

DURING the spring of 1949 I made a three-month lecture tour through the United States, accompanied by my wife. The invitation for the trip came first from Cornell University. It was later extended to include sixteen other universities and scientific institutions, and was supported jointly by them and the Rockefeller Foundation. My only regret was that time did not permit me to accept similar invitations from several other universities in the United States and Canada.

This book offers the text of three lectures given at Cornell University, at the American Museum of Natural History, New York City, and at the University of Minnesota; only the third lecture was presented at the remaining universities. It is a pleasure to be able to present the problems discussed in these lectures to a larger circle. Of course it was impossible in three lectures to describe the detailed experimental basis for the conclusions reached after almost forty years of work, much of which was carried out in collaboration with the co-workers and colleagues mentioned in the following pages. Hence a bibliography is included so that the reader can obtain more information about the findings and about our methods.

I am deeply indebted to Dr. D. R. Griffin of Cornell University for the careful planning and advance preparations for our trip, and for assistance with the English of the manuscript. Furthermore, I wish to express my thanks to all the other people whose co-operation made this lecture tour so interesting and useful to us. For many years, we have missed such contacts and the exchange of ideas with foreign countries. Scientific work must be international and cannot prosper if confined in a cage. I have learned more during these three months, in both personal and scientific matters, than in the three previous years at home.

We shall never forget the great kindness and hospitality of everyone we met in your beautiful country.

KARL VON FRISCH

Munich
May 1, 1950

Contents

[x]

I. The Color Sense of Bees

THE HONEYBEE, living in its beehive, is a social insect. In an ordinary beehive there are about sixty thousand bees, but only one is a fully developed female. This

Figure 1. Left to right: The queen. The worker bee. The drone. *H* = head, *Th* = thorax, *Ab* = abdomen, *A* = antenna, *E* = eye.

is the queen, the only egg-laying insect in the colony. The males or drones are larger, more plump, and a little stupid and lazy. All of the remaining bees are workers (Figure 1). The workers are not able to produce eggs, under normal circumstances, for their ovaries are small and undeveloped; but in other respects they are females, with the typical instincts of females; they do all the work in the hive. They feed the larvae, they build the honey-comb, they are the charwomen of the hive; and it is only these worker bees that fly out to gather honey and pollen as food for the colony.

The worker bees find the food by visiting flowers. Here some gather nectar droplets with a high concentration of sugar. Others collect pollen, since they also need protein for the growing larvae. But in taking their food

Figure 2. Left: Grass blossoms as an example of blossoms pollinated by the wind.
Figure 3. Right: The blossoms pollinated by insects are the larger and more conspicuously colored ones.

they do not behave like plunderers. They reciprocate and perform a service for the plants by effecting the pollination—flying from one flower to the next and carrying the pollen adhering to their bodies.

It is well known that there are two main types of "flowers" among the higher plants. Many plants have small green blossoms without any scent, and the transfer of pollen is effected by the air (Figure 2). Such plants produce an abundance of pollen, which is spread by the wind and comes by chance to other blossoms of the same species. Other plants have conspicuous, brightly colored blossoms or a striking scent, or both, and it is these that we ordinarily call flowers (Figure 3). Only such flowers produce nectar and are therefore visited by insects, which effect the pollination by flying from one flower to the next (Figure 4). Biologists have long believed that flowers are colored and scented to make them more striking for their insect visitors. In this way the insects can more easily find the flowers and get their food; and the pollination is also assured.

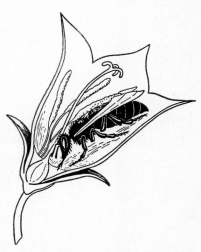

Figure 4. Nectar is produced in the bottom of a flower, so that as they suck it up the visiting insects come in contact with the pollen.

But this view has not been accepted by all biologists. About 1910 a famous ophthalmologist, Professor C. von Hess, performed many experiments on fishes, insects, and other lower animals. He tested them while they were in a positively phototactic condition—that is, under circumstances where they moved into the brightest available light. He found that in a spectrum the animals always collected in the green and the yellow-green region, which is the brightest part of the spectrum for a color-blind human eye. Therefore, von Hess asserted, fishes and invertebrates, and in particular bees, are totally color-blind. If this were true, the colors of flowers would have no biological significance. But I could not believe it, and my skepticism was the first motive which led me to begin my studies of bees about forty years ago. I tried to find out whether bees have a color sense.

By the scent of a little honey it is possible to attract bees to an experimental table. Here we can feed them on a piece of blue cardboard, for example. They suck up the food and, after carrying it back to the hive, give it to the other bees. The bees return again and again to the rich source of food which they have discovered. We let them do so for some time, and then we take away the blue card scented with honey and put out two new, clean pieces of cardboard at the site of the former feeding place—on the left a blue card, and on the right a red one. If the bees remember that they found food on blue, and if they are able to distinguish between red and blue, they should now alight on the blue card. This is exactly what happens (Figure 5).

This is an old experiment. It indicates that bees can distinguish colors, but it does not prove that they have a color sense, or color perception, for these are not always the same. Thus there are totally color-blind men, although they are very rare. They see objects as we would

Figure 5. Bees fed previously on a blue card in the middle of the table (*) alight on the clean blue cardboard without food (*left*). They distinguish it from a red cardboard (*right*).

see them in a black-and-white photograph. Yet they can distinguish between red and blue, for red appears very dark to them, and blue much lighter. Hence we cannot learn from the experiment with bees which I have just described whether the bees have distinguished red from blue by color or by shade, as a color-blind man might do. To a totally color-blind man each color appears as a gray of a certain degree of brightness. We do not know what the brightness of our various pieces of colored cardboard may be for a color-blind insect. Therefore we perform the following experiment.

On our table we place a blue card and around it we arrange gray cards of all shades from white to black.

On each card we set a little watch glass, but only the glass dish on the blue card contains food (sugar-water). In this way we train the bees to come to the color blue. Since bees have a very good memory for places we frequently change the relative positions of the cards. But the sugar is always placed on the blue card so that in every case the color indicates where food is to be found. After some hours we perform the decisive experiment. The cards and the glass dishes soiled by the bees are taken away. We place on the table a new series of clean cards of different shades of gray, each with an empty glass dish, and somewhere among them we place a clean, blue card provided, like all the others, with an empty glass dish. The bees remember the blue color and alight only on the blue card, distinguishing it from all shades of gray. This means that they have a true color sense.

This type of experiment has been criticized on the ground that the blue cardboard might have a specific scent by which the bees could recognize it. We cannot perceive any odor, but this does not prove that it is odorless for bees; we must therefore consider the possibility that the bees found the blue cardboard by smell, and not by color. But this is not the case. For we can repeat the experiment with a glass plate lying over the cards; if there were any scent it could not pass through the glass. But the outcome of the experiment is just the same as before (Figure 6).

Training bees to come to food on orange, yellow, green, violet, or purple cardboard gives the same positive result. However, if we try to train bees to find their food on scarlet red, they alight not only on the red cardboard but also on black and on all the dark-gray cards in our arrangement. Thus red and black are the same to the eye of the bee; in other words, bees are red-blind. From

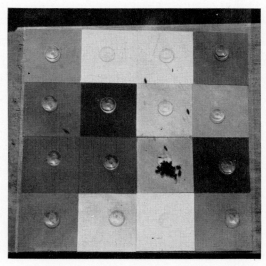

Figure 6. Bees trained to the color blue alight on a clean blue cardboard without food and under glass—distinguishing it from all degrees of gray.

these experiments it is clear that bees have a color sense, but that it is not quite the same as that of a normal human being.

To find out something more about the nature of color perception in bees, we modify our experiment. We train bees to find food on blue, and then we put on the table all the *colored* cards we have on hand, but no gray cards at all. The bees seek for blue, but it is surprising to see that they are unable to find it with certainty. They confuse blue cards with violet and purple ones. Furthermore, bees trained to yellow alight not only on yellow cards but on orange and green ones, too. If trained to orange, they actually prefer to alight on yellow, and the same happens if they are trained to green. It seems that to the eye of the bee orange, yellow, and green are the same color, and that our yellow cards are a more saturated color for them and therefore apparently more striking and attractive than orange or green. Bees which have been trained to blue, purple, or violet seem to find blue and purple more attractive than violet (von Frisch, 1915).

In 1927 Professor A. Kühn repeated my training experiments, but instead of colored cards he used a spectrum. He was able to confirm my results: that bees are red-blind, that they can distinguish other colors from all shades of gray, and that they confuse yellow with orange and green, or blue with violet. But by using spectral colors he discovered two new facts: First, he noted that there is a third quality of color in the narrow blue-green region (480–500 mμ). Bees trained to blue-green distinguish it from blue and from yellow. I had overlooked this point because I had no suitable cardboard of this blue-green color. Second, he discovered a fourth quality in ultraviolet light. If bees on the experimental table are fed for some time in ultraviolet light, they alight on every spot irradiated by ultraviolet, even though this light is invisible to us; and they distinguish the ultraviolet from all shades of white or gray. It is a distinct color for the bees.

If we compare the color sense of bees and men, we find that the visible spectrum is shortened for bees in the red but that it is extended into the ultraviolet. In this way the visible region is merely shifted to shorter wave lengths. But a much more important difference is that the human eye can distinguish about sixty distinct colors in the visible spectrum, while the bee apparently sees only four different qualities of color: yellow, blue-green, blue, and ultraviolet (Figure 7).

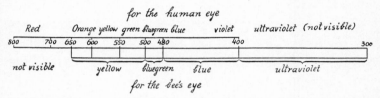

Figure 7. The colors of a spectrum for the human eye (*above*) and for the eye of the bee (*below*). The numbers indicate the wave length of light in millimicra (one micron = 0.0001 cm or ½25000 inch).

It is interesting to consider the colors of flowers in relation to the color sense of bees. We can understand at once why scarlet-red flowers are so rarely found in Europe, since the visiting insects are red-blind. There are, however, many scarlet-red flowers in America and in Africa; but long before we had learned anything about the color sense of insects it was known that this shade of red is typical of flowers visited and pollinated by birds. We know from the experiments of Honigmann that the eyes of birds are especially sensitive to red.

Many of the flowers in Europe which we call red are really purple and appear blue to bees. There are also a few species of plants in Europe with blossoms of a clearer red.[1] Biologists found long ago that these very flowers were visited and pollinated by butterflies. The color sense of butterflies has recently been studied by Dr. Dora Ilse; she discovered that butterflies are the only insects, as far as we know, which are not red-blind. Another apparent exception to the rule is the poppy (*Papaver*), which is frequently visited by bees although its flowers are scarlet-red. But poppies reflect the ultraviolet rays of sunlight. It is possible to show by suitable experiments that bees trained to the blossoms of the poppy are in fact recognizing the reflected ultraviolet light (Lotmar, 1933). We cannot perceive this light, and we see only the red. The bees, on the other hand, cannot perceive the red; they see only the ultraviolet. Thus the bees, although they are red-blind, nevertheless see the poppy as a colored flower—for them it has the color ultraviolet.

There are certain plants that have inconspicuous flowers and are nevertheless visited by many bees, for instance, the bilberry (*Vaccinium myrtillus* L.) and the Virginia creeper (*Ampelopsis quinquefolia* Michaux). One might perhaps infer that these flowers have a striking scent for bees, so that they can be located by the sense of smell. But to us they are odorless, and it can be shown that this is also true for bees. In experiments that I performed some years ago, I found that the color of the green flowers of the bilberry is much changed for the

---

[1] For instance, *Adenostyles alpina* Bluff et Fingerh., many species of the genus *Dianthus*, *Daphne striata* Tratt, *Erigeron uniflorus* L., *Erigeron alpinus* L., *Silene acaulis* Jacq., and *Viscaria alpina* G. Don.

bees if we eliminate the ultraviolet rays by placing a color filter over the flowers. Although I have not yet been able to test bilberry flowers with a spectrograph, I nevertheless believe that for bees they probably have the color ultraviolet.

The responses of bees to white flowers are a little more complicated. It is always very easy to train them to a true color, but training to *white* paper or cardboard is sometimes easy and sometimes quite difficult. This peculiar fact was explained by Dr. Mathilde Hertz (1937a,b,c, 1939). She tested various white papers and found that some of them absorbed ultraviolet rays. To these papers the bees could be trained very easily. But other white papers reflected the ultraviolet, just as they did the rays visible to us. This white the bees could not remember, and they could not learn to seek it out with certainty among other shades of white and gray. Yet the human eye cannot distinguish between the two kinds of white. To understand these facts we must consider the nature of "white."

The light coming from the sun appears white; but if we pass sunlight through a prism, the light rays emerge in an orderly arrangement corresponding to their wave lengths so that we obtain a colored spectrum. If we put the colored rays together again by means of a lens, we have white once more. Thus light containing all the colored rays in the same proportions as sunlight appears white to the human eye. If we take away a certain color the other wave lengths, when united again, are no longer white. If we take away the yellow, the remaining light

looks blue, yellow being what we call the complementary color to blue (Figure 8).

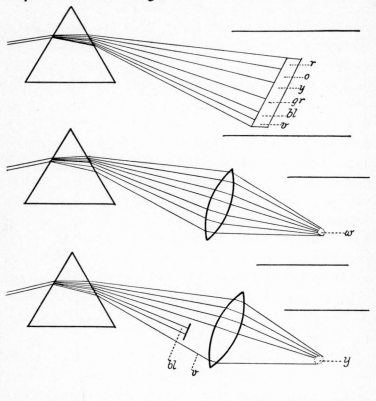

Figure 8. White light sent through a prism and put in order according to wave lengths gives a spectrum (*above*). United again by
a lens, the light becomes white once more (*center*). Without the
blue rays, the light becomes yellow (*below*).

The same may well be true for the eyes of bees. This
would mean that white light for the bee's eye must contain all wave lengths visible to bees. But we have seen

that bees are sensitive to ultraviolet rays. If the ultra-violet is taken away, the remaining light is no longer white to the bees, but has a color complementary to ultra-violet—probably blue-green. It seems that white light, containing all wave lengths visible to bees, is not striking for them; the light must apparently be colored in order to be attractive. In this connection it is interesting that nearly all white flowers do absorb ultraviolet rays, whereas yellow and blue flowers often reflect them strongly. Therefore most flowers that appear white to us are colored for bees and probably look blue-green to them.

One can see that the colors of flowers have been developed as an adaptation to the color sense of their visitors. It is evident that they are not designed for the human eye. But this should not prevent us from delighting in their beauty.

In Austria, and in Germany too, beekeepers put their beehives all together, one beneath another, to form a bee-house. In a large house with many hives, it is a little difficult for the homing bees to find their own hive; as a matter of fact, they very often shift from one hive to another. For the most part this does not matter, because bees carrying honey are welcomed everywhere. But sometimes a struggle occurs, and intruding bees may even be stung to death. A queen returning from an orientation flight or from a mating flight is in particular danger; if she alights on the wrong hive she is killed. In our country, therefore, we often see hives painted with different colors to help the bees recognize their own homes. But all beekeepers do not agree that this coloring is useful.

To study this question I placed a swarm of bees in one of a row of empty white hives and covered the front of this hive with a blue sheet of metal. On the right stood a hive that I covered with a yellow sheet, and on the left a white hive. After some days I wished to change the colors. But if I had merely interchanged the colored sheets, and if the bees had then flown to the wrong hive, I would not have known whether they were following the blue color or the scent of bees adhering to the blue sheet. Therefore the back side of the blue sheet was painted yellow, and the back of the yellow one blue. In this way I could change the colors by turning each sheet around, without moving it to a different hive. After thus reversing both metal sheets I saw many bees flying to the empty hive, which was now blue. Other bees hesitated, and after some time flew to the correct hive, despite the yellow sheet (Figure 9).

I decided that perhaps the bees were paying attention not only to their own hive but to the neighboring hives as well. In this case my experiment must have caused confusion. The bees had been accustomed to fly to a blue hive with a yellow one on the right, and a white hive on the left. Now they saw a blue hive with a yellow one on the left and a white one on the right. Here was a different arrangement; and perhaps this explained why some of the bees hesitated and finally found the correct hive by the sense of smell. I therefore repeated the experiment in another way. I reversed the blue sheet (so that it appeared yellow), but I shifted the reversed yellow sheet (which then appeared blue) from the right side to the left. The relative positions of the colors were now unchanged; the bees still found a blue hive with a yellow

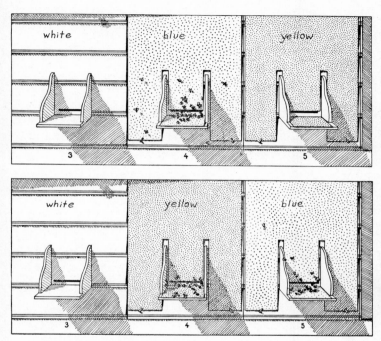

Figure 9. Upper: There is a colony of bees in the blue hive (4) situated between the white and the yellow ones, which are both empty. *Lower:* By reversing the blue sheet, the back of which was painted yellow, and also reversing the yellow sheet, which is blue on the back, the colors of the two hives have been interchanged. Many bees enter the wrong hive (5), following the color to which they are accustomed.

one on the right, and there was still a white hive to the left of the blue one (since all the hives in the row were white except those marked with my metal sheets). Un-

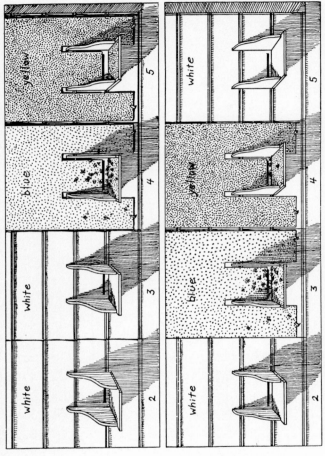

Figure 10. Upper: The initial color pattern of the blue hive (4), which is occupied by the bees, and the hives adjacent to it. *Lower:* The color of hive 4 has been changed to yellow by reversing its metal sheet, and the yellow sheet covering empty hive 5 has been turned and transferred to hive 3, which now appears blue. All of the homing bees which came from hive 4 now enter the empty hive (3) which is blue.

der these circumstances every bee, without a single exception, alighted at the wrong hive and entered it even though this hive was quite empty (Figure 10). We can see from this experiment that a painted beehive is actually a very good signpost to help bees recognize their own hive and distinguish it from others nearby (von Frisch, 1915).

But why do beekeepers disagree with one another about the effectiveness of colored hives? Simply because they have not considered the nature of the color sense of bees, as the flowers seem to have done. We often see hives stacked one beneath the other, one painted red and the next one black. This forms a contrast for the human eye, but the two look just alike to bees. The same confusion results when a green hive is placed beneath a yellow one. In such cases the painting of the hives is without effect, since there is no color contrast for bees. Beekeepers should use only blue, yellow, black, and white (Figure 11). Where they must use the same color repeatedly, they should change the color pattern formed by adjacent hives, because bees pay attention to the color of the neighboring hives as well as to their own. Furthermore, when a hive is to be painted white, it is important to choose the proper white. Zinc white seems to be suitable for this purpose because it absorbs ultraviolet and therefore looks blue-green to the bees. Lead white reflects ultraviolet and thus it is really white for bees, and hence less striking than a true color.

Beekeepers in the United States do not use beehouses, but place their beehives on the ground at considerable distances from one another, in the open. I have sometimes seen many beehives placed in a meadow without any striking landmarks around them. I do not know whether this matter has been studied experimentally, but it is probable that here too the bees may often confuse their home with other hives. I believe that painting the hives

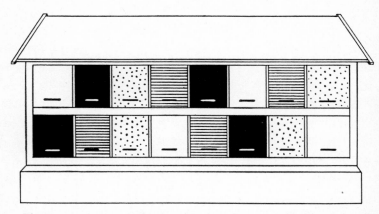

Figure 11. An example showing how to paint beehives so that it becomes as easy as possible for the bees to find their home. Colors used are white, blue, yellow, and black.

according to the principles explained above would be as useful to American beekeepers as to their European colleagues.

But let us return to the colors of flowers. What is their biological significance? Biologists have long believed that color plays an important role in making flowers attractive to bees and other insects. This is certainly true for bees flying out in search of new flowers from which to gather food. My collaborator, Dr. Therese von Öttingen (1949), set up a beehive in a courtyard with a roof of fine-mesh screening, and studied bees that had never before visited flowers and had never had the opportunity to leave the observation room. She displayed colored papers at several points in the room, and at other points she placed scented flowers which could be smelled by the bees but which were covered and could not be seen. A few of the bees were scouts, and these were attracted to both the colors and the scented flowers. From this it is clear that both odors and colors are attractive to bees that are seeking new feeding places.

We were surprised to find that very few bees—only the scouts—paid any attention at all to the flowers or to the colors and scents that were displayed. In forty experiments, lasting forty-five hours altogether, Dr. von Öttingen used hundreds of bees and fifteen different species of flowers; but she found that a group of flowers was visited by only one or two bees per hour (average, 1.27). The maximum was six bees during one hour. The great majority of the worker bees did *not* seek food even though there was very little nourishment available in the hive. As with human beings, pioneers seem to be rare in the beehive. Most individuals prefer to wait for the discoveries of a few scouts in order to find food by following their instructions, as I shall describe in the third chapter.

But colors can be useful to bees in still another way. We often find flowers in which the entrance to the tube containing the nectar is of a different appearance from the remainder of the flower—either a darker or lighter shade or, very often, a different color. It is remarkable that the color difference in nearly every case results in an impressive contrast for the eye of the bee. In German we call such colored spots *Saftmale*—sap spots. In English, I believe one would call them "nectar guides" (Figure 12). More than 150 years ago C. K. Sprengel concluded that these colored spots were signposts helping visiting insects to find the nectar. Later biologists were often skeptical about this point. But I believe that Sprengel was right, because one can test the matter by a simple experiment. If we put upon a table a large blue card on which we have placed a small yellow spot, this spot is attractive to bees and they prefer to alight on such a little spot to seek for food (W. Kellermayer [2]). In the same way they probably prefer the sap spot or nectar guide of a type of flower that they have never visited before.

Figure 12. The blue flowers of the forget-me-not (*Myosotis*) have a yellow ring (sap spot) around the entrance to the nectar.

The colors of flowers are useful in a third way—and this, I believe, is the most important one. When bees have begun to visit a flower they remain faithful to this type of flower for many days,

[2] Not yet published.

or even for many weeks; a given individual bee on its foraging trips always visits a particular species of flower. This is of advantage to the bees, which find on all blossoms of the same species the same flower mechanism and save time through being familiar with it. It is also of advantage to the flowers, for their pollination depends on bees coming from other flowers of the same species. Since the bees specialize in certain flowers, they must be able to distinguish between the various species present on their feeding grounds. Color is surely an important aid to bees in recognizing a particular kind of flower, but not an infallible guide. There is a difficulty unknown to earlier biologists. We have learned that bees cannot distinguish as many different colors as we can: only four, instead of approximately sixty. It is therefore impossible for them to recognize a certain kind of flower merely by its color, for there are likely to be other blossoms which have the same color for bees. Hence they must have other means of distinguishing the different species of flowers with certainty.

Perhaps the shape of a flower is the means by which a bee distinguishes it from other species. To find out if this is true, I trained bees to recognize a certain pattern of colored paper pasted around the entrance of a cardboard box containing sugar-water. To other boxes, without food, I attached papers of the same color but cut in different patterns. Using the patterns shown in Figure 13, I succeeded within a short time in training bees to go to the box marked with one of these figures. For example, in one experiment food was made available for some time

row of Figure 14 the length of the boundary is considerable; these are extended figures. The bees seem to notice whether a figure is very much broken or is compact. But they do not perceive in what manner the patterns differ from one another in other respects. Thus their form perception is based on wholly different criteria from ours, a fact that may be related to the different optical arrangements of the compound eye of the insect on the one hand and the cameralike human eye on the other. But the chief reason for the difference may well be that bees see the patterns during flight. Since a bee's eye is rigidly fixed on its head, a broken pattern probably gives a flickering visual impression as the bee flies past. In fact, recent experiments by H. Autrum (1948, 1949) have clearly demonstrated that this is actually the case. Thus one can understand how the brokenness of a pattern, rather than its shape, may be the important basis for form perception.

Now, the flowers of different kinds of plants often show a similar degree of brokenness of pattern even when their shapes are clearly different to our eyes; hence the form of flowers cannot serve for bees as a precise means of distinguishing between the different species, any more than can their colors. Bees must have some other, better, and more reliable means of recognizing flowers besides form and color. Could this not be the scent, which is so characteristic of each flower? Such considerations led me to study the sense of smell in bees, and I shall describe this work in the next chapter.

II. *The Chemical Senses of Bees*

IN THE first chapter I mentioned the fact that when a bee is visiting flowers it usually restricts its visits to a single species of plant. This is of advantage to the bee, since it encounters the same familiar mechanism within the blossoms. It is also very important for the plants, for it assures that the pollen brought by bees originates in other flowers of the same species. How is it possible for bees to recognize one species of flower among all the others that may be in bloom nearby? There are flowers of many colors and shades, but the eye of the honeybee distinguishes only four colors: yellow, blue, blue-green, and ultraviolet. Nor, as explained in the previous chapter, can the shapes of flowers provide adequate criteria for distinguishing between the various species. Perhaps bees select flowers by means of their specific scent. Almost every kind of blossom has an odor which a man can distinguish from that of all other flowers. But we did not know, when I first became interested in such problems, whether the same is true for bees. We were not even certain whether bees could perceive the odors of flowers at all.

In studying this problem we may train bees to odors just as I had trained them to patterns, using experiments of the following kind. On an experimental table we place some cardboard boxes, each of which can be opened from above, and each provided with a hole in the front as an entrance for the bees (Figures 15 and 16). In one

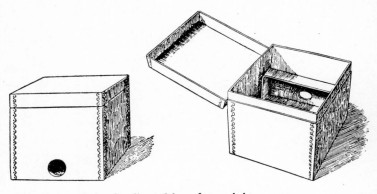

Figure 15. Left: Cardboard box for training to a scent.
Figure 16. Right: Cardboard box, opened. In training to the scent of an essential oil a small amount of this oil is dropped on the cardboard strip above the entrance to the box.

of the boxes we place a dish containing sugar-water and also a fragrant flower or a few drops of some essential oil. We change the position of this food box frequently to avoid training the bees to come to a certain place, for we wish only the odor to guide them to the food.

After several hours we take away all the boxes soiled by the bees and set out a new group of clean boxes. Into one of them we drop a little of the scent that we have been using for training purposes, but now this box, like all the others, contains no food. The bees fly from one box to another, smelling around their openings. But they actually enter only the scented box. It is evident that they can smell this odor and that they use it as a guide to the source of food.

Next I wished to find out whether bees can distinguish as many different scents as we can. I therefore trained them to an essential oil made from the skins of Italian oranges. After one day of training I placed 24 boxes on the table (Figure 17), but only one contained the

Figure 17. Arrangement for an experiment to learn whether bees are able to distinguish between several different scents.

training scent, while the others were provided with 23 different essential oils. Afterwards I repeated the experiment with the same training scent and 23 new odors that had never previously been associated with food. In both experiments we counted the number of bees visiting the boxes during five minutes of observation. The box containing the training scent was entered by 205 bees in the first experiment and by 120 in the second.

Of all the other 46 boxes only three proved attractive to the bees, and these contained the following three essential oils: "Essence de Cedrat" (148 visitors), "Essence de Bergamotte" (93 visitors), and an essential oil made from the skins of Spanish oranges (60 visitors). Only a few bees entered the remaining 43 boxes, or in some cases none at all.

These last three essential oils, which did attract a number of bees, were the only ones which were made from fruits of the same genus (*Citrus*) as the training scent. Their odor was very similar for the human nose and quite different from all the other scents. In a long series of further experiments it developed that the odor of the essential oil made from the skins of Italian oranges (the training scent) was noticeably preferred to the odors of Spanish oranges, Cedrat, or Bergamotte, but the difference in the numbers of bees attracted to these four scents was quite small.

From these and other experiments we may conclude that bees can distinguish between different qualities of odor just as well as a person whose sense of smell is very well developed. Furthermore, it seems clear that odors which are similar for the human nose are also similar for bees. In other experiments it turned out that substances without odor for us are likewise odorless for bees. The anatomy of the organs of olfaction is entirely different in bees and men, so it is surprising that their olfactory reactions are nevertheless so nearly the same (von Frisch, 1919).

Where are the sense organs of smell located in bees? Entomologists have known for a long time that insects can no longer react to scents if their antennae or "feelers" are cut off. The antennae were therefore believed by some to be the organs of olfaction. Other entomologists objected that such experiments were invalid because each antenna contains a relatively large nerve and because the cutting of this nerve would be a severe shock to the insect. The lack of response to odors might result from this shock and not from any loss of the sense of smell. There were conflicting views about this matter for many years. But it was possible to decide between them in the following way. Bees were trained to a certain odor, for example, peppermint oil. For these experiments cardboard boxes would have been cumbersome, since I wished to capture bees at the feeding dishes and operate upon them. I therefore used an arrangement like that described in the previous chapter for training bees to color. The bees found the sugar solution in a small feeding dish placed in the open on a scented piece of cardboard. Close by were other pieces of cardboard with a different scent and without any food (Figure 18). After

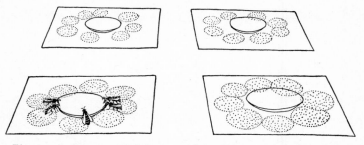

Figure 18. Bees are fed from a glass dish surrounded by a few drops of peppermint oil. The three other cards are provided with empty glass dishes and with another essential oil.

a few hours the bees were able to distinguish the training scent from the other odor and seek out the correct card with certainty.

Next I caught trained bees just as they returned from the hive to the feeding place and cut off their antennae.

When set free again, these bees continued to seek for the food but could no longer find it. Food was discovered only by chance—they were no more likely to visit the card with the training scent than any of the others. Such bees did not behave as though they were suffering from shock; they continued their search for food with vigor and persistence (Figure 19). But to be certain, I

Figure 19. The antennae have been cut off one of the bees that had been trained to the scent of peppermint oil. This bee is seeking for the training scent, but cannot find it.

trained other bees to find food on a blue card and then I removed their antennae. These bees found the blue card without hesitation and never confused it with a yellow one (Figure 20). This proved that the operation did not cause any severe shock, for the bees could still remember what they had learned but could not recognize a scent. In other words, the sense of smell is really located on the antennae.

A glimpse through the microscope shows that the antennae of bees are densely covered by sense organs, some of which are organs of touch and others organs of smell

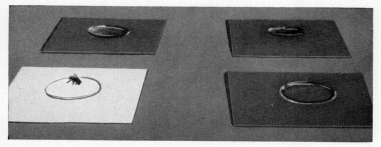

Figure 20. After being trained to the blue color a bee remembers what she has learned, in spite of the operation (cutting off antennae). She can distinguish the blue card (*lower left*) from the yellow ones, and alights on the empty glass dish seeking for food.

(Figures 21 and 22). The structure of the latter is such that the cuticle over the nerve endings is very thin, facilitating the penetration of an odorous substance (Figure

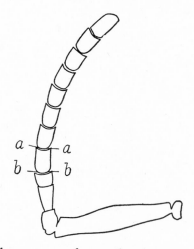

Figure 21. The antenna of a worker bee. After cutting along the line *aa* there is only one segment left that bears sense organs of smell. After cutting along the line *bb* no sense organs of smell remain on this antenna.

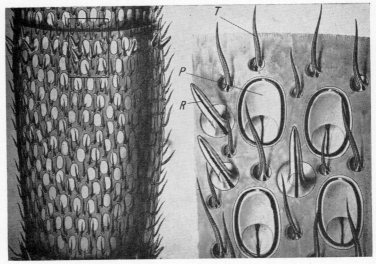

Figure 22. Left: One segment of the antenna at high magnification showing the sense organs. *Right:* The small portion outlined by black lines in the left-hand figure, greatly enlarged. T = organ of the sense of touch, R = cone-shaped organs of the sense of smell, P = pore plates (other organs of the sense of smell).

23). These sense organs are not found on the long basal stalk, or scape, of the antenna or on the first three segments of its flexible, distal part, which is called the flagellum. They are confined to the eight outer or distal segments of the flagellum. When I cut off the eight distal segments of one antenna (Figure 21,bb) and seven from the other (Figure 21,aa), the bee was still able to distinguish the training scent from other odors; it could even be trained to a new scent. But if the eighth distal segment of the second antenna was cut away the sense of smell was entirely lost. This experiment also shows that the effects of cutting away the antennae cannot be due solely

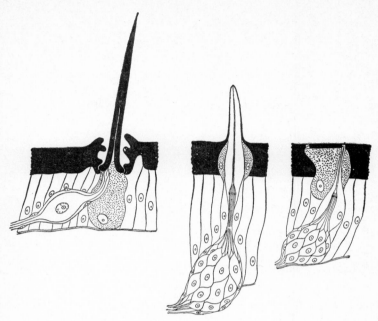

Figure 23. Left: Section through an organ of the sense of touch. The nerve ending is situated at the base of the hair and is stimulated when the hair is moved. *Center and right:* Organs of the sense of smell (cone and pore plate). The nerves ending at a very thin part of the chitin can be stimulated by scented substances diffusing through. Black = chitin cuticula.

to shock; the results can only be understood if we assume that the sense of smell is located on the antennae (von Frisch, 1921).

Most other insects also have the organs of smell confined to their antennae. But in several cases there are olfactory organs on other appendages of the head as well, i.e., on the palps of butterflies and of the water beetle *Dytiscus.*

I also tried to measure the sensitivity of the sense of smell in bees by training them to a certain odor and then diluting it more and more until they could no longer distinguish between scented and unscented boxes. When the dilution had reached a stage where the odor was no longer perceptible to us, we found that the bees too had lost the ability to perceive it. Thus the olfactory sensitivity of bees is roughly the same as that of human beings. We may be sure, therefore, that the scent of most flowers is insufficient to attract bees from a great distance.

The role of the sense of smell was well illustrated, however, by experiments of the following type. I trained bees to distinguish a scented box with a blue front (Figure 24, above) placed among several others that were neither scented nor colored. Then I replaced this box with two others, on the right an uncolored box containing the scent and on the left an unscented box which was colored blue (Figure 24, below). The bees flew directly toward the blue box, but at a distance of about an inch they hesitated, apparently seeking for the scent to which they were accustomed. Then they inspected the other boxes, and when they approached the scented one they alighted and went inside. Apparently the color was visible from a greater distance, but the scent seemed to be the more convincing of the two. Likewise, the color of flowers has the advantage that it can attract bees from a greater distance, while the scent is specific for each species and thus permits the definite recognition of the flowers at close range (von Frisch, 1919).

There is one respect in which the sense of smell in bees

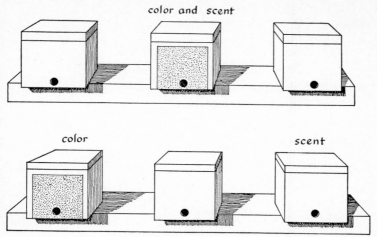

color and scent

color

scent

Figure 24. Bees are trained to a scented box with blue cardboard surrounding the hole (*above, middle box*). Afterwards, during the experiment, they find the blue color on the left and the scent on the right of the former feeding place (*below*). They fly toward the color from a distance of some meters, but they enter only the scented box.

is certainly superior to ours. The human organ of smell is located inside the nasal chamber, and the particles of odorous substances are brought to it by the stream of air utilized for breathing. Since this air stream is well mixed on its way into the nose, there can be no correlation between the shape of a scented object and the sensation of odor that it arouses. But in bees the olfactory organs are located on the antennae, and these can be moved about. Furthermore, the antennae are also covered by organs of the sense of touch, so that the sense of smell stands in a close relation to that of touch. A round scented object may give quite a different sensation to a bee than will an angular one. August Forel many years ago stated that bees might "smell" the form of objects as a result of this close relationship between the receptor organs of touch and smell on the antennae. The bee's association of touch and smell would be analogous to our own constant integration ever since infancy of what we see with our eyes and what we feel with our hands.

This association of touch and smell is very useful to bees as they visit flowers. Often they bring their antennae close to the flower, almost in contact with it, so that they can probably perceive even quite feeble odors. Moreover, if various parts of a flower have different scents, the bee can distinguish and locate these separate portions in a very precise manner. With this in mind I wondered whether there might be sap spots or nectar guides not only for the eye but also for the sense of smell. It was a pleasure to find that in many blossoms this was really true. In a narcissus, for instance, the yellow nectar guide (Figure 25) is not only of a different color from the white corolla but of a different scent as well. If we separate the yellow parts of the flower from the white parts and train some bees to one of these scents, they can distinguish between the two with certainty. And we too can perceive the difference in scent very easily once the parts have been separated, but we cannot do so by smelling the whole flower, because the two odors are mixed before reaching our olfactory organs. Bees, with their sense of smell localized on the surfaces of the antennae, can easily locate such differences and can be guided to the nectar by these scented sap spots.

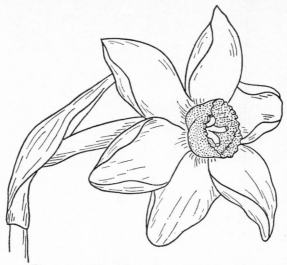

Figure 25. The white flower of *Narcissus* with a yellow sap spot (stippled).

Such scented sap spots were also found in other flowers. Often there was no difference in quality but an increasing intensity of odor around the entrance to the bottom of the flower where the nectar is located.[1]

Human beings have two types of chemical sense, smell and taste. Anatomically, our sense organs of smell are located in the nasal chamber and those of taste on the tongue; they are supplied by different nerves. Physiologically, we can perceive through our sense of smell so many different qualities of odor that we even lack words to designate individual odors; but the sense of taste (when unaided by odors of foods) can distinguish only

---

[1] Experiments carried out by Miss Mathilde Huber and Miss Therese Lex but not yet published.

four qualities: sweet, bitter, sour, and salty. Moreover, the sense of smell is much more sensitive than that of taste. Consequently its biological significance is very different. Many animals with a well-developed sense of smell can perceive food or enemies at a considerable distance because evaporated particles can excite their olfactory receptors at very low concentrations. But chemical substances must be much more concentrated to excite the sense organs of taste, and since the latter are located in the mouth they serve for testing food when the animal is already in contact with it just before, or during, a meal.

Much the same division of the chemical senses into two types is found in bees and other insects. The sense organs on the antennae can detect, as far as we know, about as many different qualities of odor as the human nose. Since they are very sensitive they are able to detect food and other objects from some distance. But bees also have sense organs of taste located on the mouth parts in order to examine food when it is taken up. Bees can recognize a sweet solution only when they come in contact with it, but they are rather fastidious about sweetness. If offered a solution containing 20 per cent sucrose (about two-thirds molar), bees ordinarily suck it up. If it contains 10 per cent, we can see that there is an individual difference in taste—just as with men. Some bees drink, some hesitate, and others refuse it altogether. If a solution contains 5 per cent, they taste it but refuse to suck it up. This is their *threshold of acceptance*, and it varies depending on the feeding conditions. If there are many plants in bloom, one finds a high threshold of acceptance—sometimes about 40 per cent. During the fall when flowers become scarce there is a threshold of about 5 per cent. Bees, like men, become more fastidious under better conditions.

There is another limit, the *threshold of perception*, apparently the lowest concentration which will stimulate the sense of taste at all. This is invariable under good and poor conditions alike. To measure this threshold it is only necessary to starve the bees for several hours. Then they are ready to accept any solution that tastes noticeably sweet to them. For hungry bees the threshold is always between 1 and 2 per cent (von Frisch, 1934).

It is significant, biologically, that bees do not collect for storage in the hive solutions with a low concentration of sugar, although they may use them for their own nourishment. If stored in the honeycombs such solutions would not keep until winter. Indeed, all honey is chemically different from the nectar out of which it was made, and one important difference is an increase in sugar concentration by the elimination of water. Dilute sugar solutions require excessive periods of time, or excessive effort by the bees, in order to convert them into honey. Flowers have become adapted to this need by producing nectar with a high concentration of sugar (on the average about 40 per cent—R. Beutler, 1930).

Chemists have learned that there are many different sugars, most of which taste sweet to human beings. But out of thirty-four sugars and sugarlike chemical compounds that we tested, only nine are sweet for bees: cane

sugar, malt sugar, grape sugar, fructose, trehalose, mele-
sitose, fucose, alpha-methylglucoside, and inositol. Most
of the sugars which are sweet to us are tasteless to bees,
for when offered either in pure condition or mixed with
cane sugar, they have the same effect as pure water. This
I found to be true for the following substances (those
indicated with an asterisk are slightly repellent to bees):
lactose, melibiose, cellobiose,* gentiobiose,* raffinose,
tetraglycosan,* tetra laevan,* glycogen, galactose, man-
nose, sorbose, rhamnose, xylose, l-arabinose, d-arabinose,
trimethylglucose,* beta-methylglucoside,* beta-methyl-
fructoside,* beta-methylgalactoside, alpha-methylman-
noside, erythritol, quercitol, mannitol, sorbitol, and
dulcitol. It was not possible to determine definite rules
valid for all insects governing the sweetness of these
compounds, for substances which are sweet to one insect may be tasteless to others. For instance, the trisac-
charide raffinose is tasteless to bees, but to ants it is the
sweetest sugar of all those we have tested.

Honeybees are able to distinguish not only sweet but
salty, sour, and bitter tastes as well. If we add salt to sugar-
water the bees refuse it. I tried several methods to test the
sensitivity of bees to salt. I could find the quantity of
salt which had to be added to a sugar solution to cause
its rejection, or, better, the amount which caused bees
to hesitate slightly as they sucked up the solution. But a
still better method is the following one, which depends
upon the fact that bees take up larger volumes of solution if the sugar concentration is high. The sweeter the
taste, the more they pump into their honey stomachs.

For example, one of my experiments carried out on September 9, 1929, gave the following results, which are best presented in tabular form.

Number of bees	Concentration of sugar solution	Average volume of solution taken up per visit
70	17% (0.5 molar)	42 cubic millimeters
55	34% (1 molar)	55 cubic millimeters
49	68% (2 molar)	61 cubic millimeters

To find the threshold concentration of salt which the bees can barely taste, I offered them two dishes; both contained the same sugar solution, but one of the dishes also contained a very little salt. The amount of salt in the second dish was so low that the bees did not hesitate to take up the mixed solution, but they took less of it than of the pure sugar syrup. Apparently the pure solution tasted better. This sort of experiment enabled us to measure the very low concentrations at which they could taste the salt.

In another typical experiment performed on September 17, 1929, the bees were fed 0.5 molar sucrose, and again sucked up an average of 42 cubic millimeters per visit. Then, immediately afterwards, they were presented with a solution containing the same concentration of sugar plus 0.03 molar, or 0.017 per cent, salt (NaCl); from this mixed solution they took up only 37 cubic millimeters per visit. When the same test was repeated a year later the figures I obtained were 44 and 37 cubic millimeters, respectively. Even when a half-molar sucrose solution contains only 0.015 molar NaCl, the bees take up less than they take from pure half-molar sucrose. But the difference disappears if we use as little as 0.0075 molar NaCl.

I concluded from these experiments that honeybees are a little more sensitive to salt than are human beings. The same is true for materials which taste sour. But to bitter substances the bees are much less sensitive than we. They seem to enjoy a mixture of quinine and sugar which is so disgusting to the human sense of taste that anyone would spit it out at once (von Frisch, 1934).

With this in mind, I thought that I might be able to help the public authorities in the following way. In many countries beekeepers are allowed to buy sugar at low cost to feed their bees for the wintertime. Such encouragement to beekeeping serves to increase the number of colonies kept through the winter and thus improves honey production and the pollination of flowers and certain crop plants. But the cheap sugar thus placed at the disposal of beekeepers is supposed to be used only in the beehive, and not in the kitchen. To assure that this sugar was used only as intended, especially during the war years, it was desirable to mix something with the sugar which would make it useless for human consumption. But it was not easy to find a suitable denaturing substance. Either a compound was not efficient in producing a bad taste for men, or it had a disagreeable taste for bees as well. I proposed that the sugar be mixed with a small amount of octoacetylsucrose, which I had found to be very bitter for men but tasteless to bees. There was an initial difficulty in that this was a rare and expensive substance. But the chemical industry was able to work out a method for its production at low cost, and it was given the trade name "Octosan." It proved especially suitable for our purpose because it was a chemical compound of sucrose and acetic acid, and therefore quite harmless for both bees and men. Moreover, during the honey-ripening process in the beehive it decomposed after several weeks, so that its bitter taste was not imparted to the honey (O. Wahl, 1937).

Octosan was introduced in Slovakia, Bohemia, Poland, Romania, Bulgaria, Holland, and Belgium, and it proved practicable over a number of years. But in other countries the beekeepers would not agree to feed their precious bees such disgusting sugar. Perhaps some of them disliked this type of sugar chiefly because it was not useful for cooking.

It can be shown that salty, sour, and bitter are different qualities of taste for bees, just as they are for men. But the methods are somewhat complicated, because it is impossible to train bees to find food by taste as we trained them to find it by color or by odor. Let me cite only one example showing how we could determine that bitter and salty are different qualities of taste for bees. To a certain sugar solution we added just enough salt so that the bees rejected the mixture. Then we did the same for bitter, preparing a mixture of sugar and quinine just bitter enough to prevent the bees from accepting it. If these two substances had the same taste for bees, our two solutions should have aroused the same sensation of taste. However, we could show that this was not the case. For if we starved the bees, they took up a bitter mixture containing eight times more quinine than before. But these hungry bees showed no change in the threshold of refusal for mixtures of salt and sugar. Hungry bees will tolerate more bitterness, but they will not take a higher concentration of salt. Bitter and salty, therefore, cannot be the same quality of taste for bees. In a similar fashion it can be proved that sour is also a distinct quality of taste (von Frisch, 1934).

The fact that insects can distinguish four qualities of taste (sweet, bitter, salty, and sour) can also be demonstrated directly by experiments with water beetles (*Hydrous piceus, Dytiscus latissimus,* and *Cybister laterimarginalis*). These insects when seeking their food in the water can perceive the taste of food as it diffuses from some distance. Hence one can train them to find sources of food by the sense of taste. Water beetles trained to find food along with salty-, sour-, sweet-, or bitter-tasting substances can distinguish any one of these tastes with certainty from the other three qualities (E. Ritter, 1936; L. Bauer, 1939).

Some animals have sense organs of taste not only in or near the mouth but on other parts as well. Professor D. E. Minnich of the University of Minnesota found (1922a) that butterflies could taste with the tips of their legs. If a butterfly steps into a sweet substance it instantly stretches out its proboscis, and often begins to feed. In this case the sense of taste is adapted to detect food as well as to regulate its intake. Therefore a lower threshold seems to be useful, for even a small amount of sugar can serve as a guide to a source of food. As a matter of fact, the taste receptors on the legs of butterflies are the most sensitive ones known to date. In flies, and other insects too, we find a well-developed sense of taste on the tips of the legs (D. E. Minnich, 1922b, 1929; F. Haslinger, 1935).

Among the vertebrates we find low thresholds for the sense of taste only among the fishes. This fact is also related to the feeding habits of fish, for substances dissolved in water can guide a fish to food even from considerable distances. If the food is at some distance, materials diffusing from it reach the fish in a highly diluted state. Molecules from such food may reach any part of a fish's body, so we find that the sense of taste is not confined to the mouth, as in higher vertebrates, but is widely distributed over the surface of the body. *Trigla*, a bottom-dwelling fish, presents an analogy to the butterflies, for it is especially adapted for tasting materials lying at the bottom of the waters where it lives. Some of the rays of its pectoral fins are developed into finger-like structures which bear many organs of taste (Scharrer, 1935). (See Figure 26.)

To illustrate the wide variation in sensitivity of the organs of taste in various animals, Figure 27 shows the amounts of crystalline sugar which must be dissolved in one quart of water to give it a degree of sweetness just perceptible to bees, to human beings, to a minnow, and to the legs of a butterfly.

Before concluding this chapter devoted to the chemical

Figure 26. In fishes the sense of taste is not confined to the mouth. In this case (*Trigla*), certain rays of the pectoral fins are developed like fingers and bear many sense organs of taste.

Figure 27. The bottle contains one quart of water. *Left:* The quantity of sugar (sucrose) which must be dissolved in this amount of water to give it a sweetness just perceptible (*a*) for bees (0.083 molar), (*b*) for human beings (0.0125 molar), (*c*) for a fish (0.0002 molar), and (*d*) for the legs of the red admiral butterfly (0.000078 molar).

senses of bees I should like to describe some of the practical applications of this knowledge. Farmers often wish to cause more bees to fly to a certain kind of flower in order to improve its pollination. With red clover, in particular, the pollination is often very poor when fields are large. Under normal circumstances most of these flowers are visited and pollinated by bumblebees, which have a proboscis long enough to obtain all the nectar in the tubes of the clover flowers. Honeybees, therefore, often prefer other flowers which are in bloom at the same time and which are more convenient for them to feed upon. Bumblebees, on the other hand, are too scarce to effect the pollination of all the flowers in large fields of red clover.

About 1930, certain Russian scientists, knowing that it was possible to train bees to scents, developed a new method to improve the pollination of red clover. They brought beehives close to a field of red clover and trained the bees to the odor of these flowers. The training was accomplished during the evening by feeding the bees in the hive sugar solutions scented with the flowers of red clover. To obtain this scented sugar solution the Russians simply put some flowers into the sugar-water so that after several hours the odor of the clover was taken up by the solution. The flowers themselves were then strained off. Many of the bees which had been fed in this way flew to red clover plants the next morning. By using this technique the Russians managed to improve the crop of red clover to a considerable degree.

Several years earlier, I had proposed a similar method;

to explain it I must anticipate a little of the next chapter. If bees have discovered a good feeding place they announce the fact in the hive by means of certain dances performed on the honeycombs. The other bees not only learn that there is food available, but they are also informed in which flowers it is to be found. They obtain this information from the scent of the flowers which adheres to the bodies of the dancing bees. If we feed some bees at an artificial feeding place provided with the scent of the flowers that we wish them to visit, the foraging bees will perform their dances in the hive and stimulate other bees, which will fly out in search of the same odor and thus reach flowers of the same species. On this basis I expected to guide many bees to a certain field in order to secure better pollination. Because of the catastrophic shortage of food in Europe during the past few years, I studied this practical problem in cooperation with beekeepers and agricultural experiment stations. Out of several methods which gave good results let me describe only a simple one.

When a field of red clover came into bloom we brought several beehives close to the field and fed the bees every morning with a small amount of sugar-water in a box placed just in front of the hive (Figure 28). The box was divided into three compartments; the middle one contained flowers of red clover and the others contained the food (Figure 29). To reach the sugar the bees were obliged to creep through these flowers, and thus their bodies were certain to become heavily scented. Afterwards they danced in the hive, and other bees, perceiving

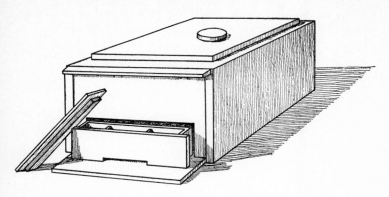

Figure 28. Beehive with feeding box, the cover of which is opened to show the three compartments inside (see Figure 29).

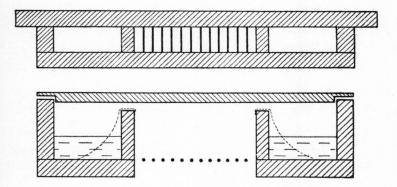

Figure 29. The feeding box, seen from above (*upper drawing*) and in cross section (*below*). The box is set in front of the entrance of the hive, so that the bees can enter and leave the hive by passing under the middle compartment of the box. The middle compartment must be filled with the flowers that one wishes to be visited by the bees. The lateral compartments contain sugar-water. To reach the sugar the bees pass the wire grid and crawl through the flowers. Afterwards, when dancing in the hive, they carry the scent of these flowers on their bodies.

⌈ 49 ⌉

from the bodies of the dancers the odor of the flowers in our feeding box, searched for red clover when they flew out to forage.

To test the effectiveness of this method we performed experiments involving two fields of red clover so far apart that the bees visiting one field could not possibly fly to the other. The quality of the soil, the size of the field, the seed, the fertilizer, and other such factors were kept as similar as possible. Near each field we placed the same number of beehives. At one field the bees were fed every morning with sugar-water provided with the scent of red clover as described above. The bees at the other field received the same amount of sugar-water, at the same time of day, but without any scent; this field served as our control. We repeated this experiment twelve times in various localities. In all cases the field where the bees were guided by odor was visited by more bees than the control field—on the average, three to four times as many. The yield could be measured in nine of the twelve experiments, and the weight of the crop averaged 40 per cent higher at the fields where scented sugar-water had been employed.

We obtained promising results in experiments with other agricultural plants as well—with Alsatian clover (*Trifolium hybridum* L.), rape (*Brassica napus* L.), turnip (*Brassica rapa* L.), and buckwheat (*Fagopyrum esculentum* Moench). However, with these plants we did not obtain sufficiently extensive data to permit definite statements as to the effectiveness of the technique; the matter should certainly be studied more thoroughly.

Procedures of this kind can be useful to beekeepers as well as to farmers. In many experiments we found that when bees were directed to seek for certain flowers the yield of honey could be increased by 50 per cent or more if they were guided in this way to flowers which were supplying a rich source of nectar. For bees which have been fed scented sugar-water seek very diligently for the flowers whose scent was used at the feeding place, and they collect nectar more industriously than bees which have been fed unscented sugar (von Frisch, 1947).

In the actual employment of these methods one must pay careful attention to many factors which I cannot discuss here in detail. But I have described this application of our findings to present a new example of a well-known fact—a fact not recognized at all times by all governments—that research work performed for its scientific interest alone often proves later to be of great practical value in ways which could never have been foreseen.

III. *The Language of Bees*

WHEN I wish to attract some bees for training experiments I usually place upon a small table several sheets of paper which have been smeared with honey. Then I am often obliged to wait for many hours, sometimes for several days, until finally a bee discovers the feeding place. But as soon as one bee has found the honey many more will appear within a short time—perhaps as many as several hundred. They have all come from the same hive as the first forager; evidently this bee must have announced its discovery at home.

I was curious to learn how bees could tell their fellows about the presence of food at a new location. But it is not possible to observe what happens as the bees crawl about between the honeycombs inside an ordinary beehive. I therefore constructed an observation hive in which the honeycombs were arranged edge to edge so that they formed one large comb, the surface of which could be watched through glass windows (Figure 30). It was also necessary to number every bee we wished to study, so that it could be recognized individually among the mass of other bees on the honeycombs. For this purpose I painted the bees with small spots of five different colors; a white spot on the front part of the thorax stood

Figure 30. The observation hive. The entrance for the bees is at the right.

for the number 1; a red, for 2; a blue, for 3; a yellow, for 4; and a green, for 5. A white spot on the hind part of the thorax indicated the number 6; a red, 7; a blue, 8; a yellow, 9; and a green, 0. By employing combinations of these colors I could apply any two-digit number; and spots to indicate the hundreds were painted on the abdomen, so that I could number as many as 599 bees at one time (Figure 31). The actual colors applied to the bees consisted of dry artist's pigment mixed with a solution of shellac in alcohol. This mixture dries quickly and adheres well to the body of a bee.

To study the behavior of bees which have just dis-

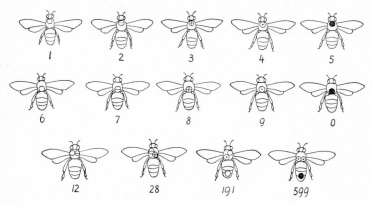

Figure 31. For numbering the bees, five different colors were used. The meanings of the symbols in the drawing are: white circle, a white spot; horizontal line in the circle, a red spot; cross in the circle, a blue spot; dot in the circle, a yellow spot; black circle, a green spot.

covered a rich source of food one may set out near the observation hive a glass dish filled with sugar-water. When a foraging worker comes to this feeding place she is marked with a colored spot while she is sucking up the sugar, so that we can recognize her later in the hive. After she has returned to the hive our marked bee is first seen to deliver most of the sugar-water to other bees. Then she begins to perform what I have called a round dance. On the same spot she turns around, once to the right, once to the left, repeating these circles again and again with great vigor. Often the dance is continued for half a minute or longer at the same spot. Frequently the dancer then moves to another spot on the honeycomb and repeats the round dance and afterwards ordinarily returns to the feeding place to gather more sugar.

During the dance the bees near the dancer become greatly excited; they troop behind her as she circles, keeping their antennae close to her body. Suddenly one of them turns away and leaves the hive. Others do likewise, and soon some of these bees appear at the feeding place. After they have returned home they also dance, and the more bees there are dancing in the hive the more appear at the feeding place. It is clear that the dance inside the hive reports the existence of food. But it is not clear how the bees that have been aroused by the dance manage to find the feeding place.

To learn whether the round dance imparts information about the direction in which food is to be found, I fed several numbered bees from my observation hive at a feeding place 10 meters to the west. At each of four points in the meadow around the hive, to the north, south, east, and west, I placed on the ground a glass dish containing sugar-water scented by a little honey. A few minutes after the start of round dances in the hive new bees appeared simultaneously at all the dishes regardless of their direction. The message brought by a bee as she performed the round dance seemed to be a very simple one, one that carried the meaning "Fly out and seek in the neighborhood of the hive."

But it is not natural for bees to gather their food from glass dishes. If we feed our numbered bees at the same feeding place with sugar solutions placed upon fresh flowers, for instance, cyclamen (Figure 32), and if the foraging bees dance after they have returned to the hive,

Figure 32. Numbered bees are fed on cyclamen flowers.

new bees fly out as before, but now they are seeking for something definite. Somewhere in the vicinity of the hive we establish an observation point by placing on the ground two large dishes; one of these contains cyclamen flowers and the other contains phlox. The newly aroused bees are interested only in the cyclamen; they take no notice of the phlox (Figure 33). Next we can change the flowers at the feeding place, putting food on blossoms of phlox. Now the same numbered bees that had previously collected sugar-water on cyclamen flowers begin to

Figure 33. The newcomers sent out by the dancing bees coming from cyclamen are interested only in this species of flower. They alight on cyclamen and seek for food there. They are not attracted to phlox or other flowers.

gather it on the phlox (Figure 34). After a few minutes the situation at the observation point changes radically:

Figure 34. Feeding on phlox.

the new bees are no longer interested in cyclamen; they alight only on phlox—examining the flowers as though convinced that they must contain food.

I succeeded in obtaining similar results from this type of experiment whenever I employed fragrant flowers, even those with a very feeble scent; but I did not succeed when I chose flowers without any odor at all. If, for instance, I fed numbered bees on the unscented blossoms of bilberry (*Vaccinium myrtillus* L.), then the new bees that swarmed out of the hive searched earnestly in the vicinity for the food that had been announced to them; but a dish of bilberry placed in the meadow did not receive any more attention than the surrounding grass or other unscented objects. The same result was obtained in other experiments with odorless blossoms (grass blossoms, *Holcus lanatus* L., the lily *Tritonia crocosmaeflora* Voss., and the Virginia creeper *Ampelopsis quinquefolia* Michaux).

On the other hand, the same result can be obtained without employing flowers at all. We can feed several numbered bees from glass dishes of sugar-water, each dish resting upon a piece of cardboard scented by peppermint oil. Nearby we also set out a series of similar cards, some scented with a few drops of peppermint oil and some with other essential oils. The new foragers are now interested only in the scent of peppermint; they alight on every place and on every object touched by this oil. Apparently the newly aroused bees learn the scent of the flowers just visited by the dancer, and when they fly out seeking for this odor they reach the same kind of flower. Here is a biological function of flower scents which had not been known before.

The new foragers remember very well the odor that they learned from the dancer, and they are able to find it with certainty. This was once demonstrated to me in striking fashion in Munich during mid-July at the systematic section of the botanical garden, where I counted seven hundred different plants blooming at the same time. One of these was *Helichrysum lanatum* DC., planted only in one small flower bed and visited only by one species of solitary bee, but never by honeybees. Biologists have reported that honeybees have never been seen gathering nectar from this particular species. But I fed some numbered bees from my observation hive at the border of the systematic section of the botanical garden, supplying sugar-water in a glass dish surrounded by several blossoms of *Helichrysum*. The dancing bees coming from this feeding place carried the odor of *Helichrysum* on their bodies. Within the following hour many honeybees visited the flower bed containing *Helichrysum lanatum* and alighted on the flowers in search of food. They had sought out the specific odor of this species among the seven hundred other scented flowers blooming nearby (von Frisch, 1923b).

The bees that troop after the returning forager as she dances on the honeycomb perceive the flower scent in two ways. By holding their antennae toward the dancer they smell the scent adhering to her body as a result of her contact with the flower. The upper surface of the bee's body has the ability to hold scents for long periods (Steinhoff, 1948). Second, during pauses in the dance, the dancer feeds the bees that are following her by regurgitating a droplet of nectar from her honey stomach. This nectar was gathered from the bottom of the flower and is saturated with its characteristic scent. The bees that have been aroused by the dancer can thus receive the odor of the flower both from her body and from the nectar that she passes to them.

The reader may well ask how we can know these details. It was actually not difficult at all to find them out by means of experiments of the following sort. We can feed unscented sugar-water to several numbered bees as they alight on cyclamen flowers. To prevent this sugar solution from taking up the odor of the surrounding cyclamen blossoms we place it in a small, spherical glass flask from which the bees can suck it up only through a narrow cleft (Figure 35, below). These bees carry the odor of cyclamen flowers only externally on their bodies, and the other bees which they send out from the hive seek for this odor. In another experiment we allow different foraging bees to alight on an odorless card and feed them in the same manner with sugar-water that we have previously exposed for one hour to the odor of cyclamen flowers (Figure 35, above). In this case the odor is carried only internally, in the honey stomach, but the bees that are aroused by the dancers again seek for cyclamen.

It is interesting to determine the relative effectiveness of these two methods of transporting the flower scent back to other bees in the hive. We can put the matter to

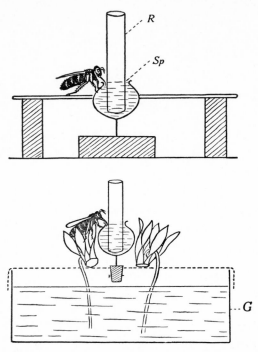

Figure 35. Below: The bee sitting on cyclamen takes up odorless sugar-water. She carries the odor only externally on the body. *G* = glass vessel containing water. *Above:* The bee sitting on a piece of unscented cardboard takes up scented sugar-water. She carries the odor only internally in the honey stomach. *R* = glass tube, *Sp* = the narrow cleft from which the food can be taken.

a test by feeding bees as they alight on cyclamen flowers with sugar-water that has been saturated with the odor of phlox blossoms. Now the scented material adhering to the body of the dancing bee will have a different odor from the nectar carried in her honey stomach. If the feeding place is close to the hive, the bees aroused by the dancer visit cyclamen flowers about as often as phlox.

But if the feeding place is farther away—for example, a half mile from the hive—the new foragers are interested only in phlox, the odor of which was carried in the honey stomach of the dancer. This means that during a long flight back to the hive the scented material adhering to the body of a bee is lost. Clearly the scent taken up with the nectar and carried in the closed honey stomach (Figure 36) is very important when bees are collecting at considerable distances (von Frisch, 1946a).

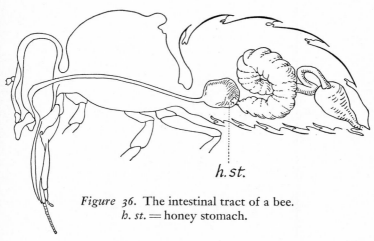

h. st.

Figure 36. The intestinal tract of a bee.
h. st. = honey stomach.

These dances are observed only if there is a rich source of food (Figure 37), so that evidently they also carry the basic meaning "There is plenty of food and sweetness." If we take away a glass dish full of sugar solution from which bees have been feeding, and replace it by another dish provided merely with some sheets of filter paper moistened from beneath by a little sugar-water, then there is a scarcity of food although the composition of

Figure 37. Plenty of food.

the solution is unchanged (Figure 38). Provided that we do not reduce the volume of sugar-water below a certain critical level, the bees will continue to collect it by suck-

Figure 38. A scarcity of food. Filter paper moistened from beneath with sugar-water by the syringe.

ing it up laboriously from the pores of the filter paper. But now they do not dance after returning to the hive, and hence no new worker bees appear at the feeding place. The same result follows if we dilute the sugar solution to a certain point, even though a large volume of the fluid is still available. The sweeter the sugar, the more vigorous are the dances (von Frisch, 1923b, 1934).

This reaction can also be observed under natural conditions when the bees are visiting flowers; and it is important for the bees, since several kinds of flowers often come into bloom at the same time. When this happens the various species may be discovered by foragers from the same hive, but those bees which have discovered the richest source of food dance most vigorously and send out the largest number of new foragers to this kind of plant. The pollination of these plants is thereby guaranteed in the best manner, and likewise the beehive has the benefit of securing the best and sweetest nectar. After the bees have harvested a rich source of food so industriously that the nectar of this species becomes scarce, the dances come to a stop and no more worker bees are sent out to visit this kind of flower. In this way the activity of the whole group of foraging bees is adjusted to the relative abundance of the nectar of various flower species.

The observations that I have just described make it clear that the dancer guides other bees to the flowers she has discovered, and uses the flower odor as an indication of the location of the rich food source. Another scent is also used for this purpose, and it is produced by the worker bee herself. Bees have a scent organ located on the abdomen in a pocket of skin lined with glands. Usually the pocket is closed and cannot give out any scent. But bees returning to a rich source of food open the scent organ as they approach the feeding place and alight upon it (Figure 39). In doing this they apparently apply

Figure 39. Three bees at the glass dish with plenty of food (sugar-water). The opened scent organ can be seen in the bee at the left beneath the arrow. The bee at the right has already withdrawn its scent organ.

to the food source a scent which is very attractive to other bees. It seems to carry the meaning "Come here; this way!" The importance of this scent when bees are visiting flowers which have no odor could be shown by the following experiment: I arranged two feeding places without scent, and at each place allowed about twelve numbered bees to collect sugar-water. At one feeding place I applied a little shellac to each bee as she arrived, so as to close the pocket containing the scent glands. These bees continued to dance in the hive just as vigorously as before, but they could not give out any scent when they returned to the feeding place. As a result I counted at this dish only one-tenth as many newcomers as at the control dish, where the bees had been allowed to use their scent organs in the normal way (von Frisch, 1923b).

For many years in performing experiments of this general kind I always placed the food in the immediate vicinity of the hive, partly for convenience and partly so that I could watch the bees at the same time both at the observation hive and at the feeding place. Occasional observations suggested that bees could also tell something about the distance from the hive to the feeding place. Since bees often gather food a mile or more from the hive, it would clearly be advantageous if a forager which had located a rich but distant source of food could convey to other bees some idea of its location as well as its odor. To study this interesting question I performed the following experiment in August, 1944. Two feeding places were arranged, one 10 meters and the other 300 meters from the hive; both were visited by numbered bees from my observation hive. In order to learn from experiments of this sort where the newly aroused foragers may actually fly in search of food, we used a scent such as lavender oil in the following way. At one of the feeding places sugar-water was offered in a glass vessel, and this vessel rested on a card scented with lavender oil (Figure 40). At different points in the meadow we also set out test cards that were without food but were supplied with small vials of the same oil. The bees aroused by dancers from the feeding place sought for this scent, and on approaching one of the test cards they would often alight upon it (Figure 41).

After this preparation I was ready to begin the actual

Figure 40. A small wooden table is used as feeding place, and it can be fixed in the ground anywhere by means of its single leg, which is pointed at the lower end. On the table is a glass dish with sugar-water, resting on a scented card. The photograph shows many bees visiting the feeding place. Usually we restricted the numbered bees to about ten for each experiment.

Figure 41. Left: The bees sent out by the dancers smell around the three tiny vials containing the same odor as that supplied at the feeding place, and they alight on the cardboard. *Right:* The drawing shows one vial containing the essential oil, set in a hole of the cardboard. *ph.* = vial, *c.* = cardboard, *e.o.* = essential oil.

experiment by giving plenty of food at the nearer feeding place, so that bees returned from a rich source at 10 meters and danced in the hive. After several minutes there were many newcomers at this feeding place and on other test cards close to it, but only a few were seen near the 300-meter site. For example, in one experiment— and by no means the most striking one—we counted 12 new bees near the feeding place 300 meters from the hive and 174 during the same time at the 10-meter site. But when we reversed the procedure, giving plenty of food at the distant source and none at 10 meters, then the only bees dancing in the hive were those fed at 300 meters. Now the newcomers appeared quickly at the distant site, while we saw only a very few at 10 meters from the hive. During one hour of observation in a typical experiment of the latter type, we counted 61 bees near the distant feeding place and only 8 near the feeding place 10 meters away. Often the difference was even greater. Hence it seemed clear that the returning foragers brought a message about the distance of the rich food source they had found.

In order to study the nature of this message we can give plenty of food at both feeding places at the same time and mark the bees collecting food at each. When we now look into the observation hive we see a truly curious sight: all the bees marked at the 10-meter food source are performing round dances just like those described above (Figure 42, left). But all the bees that have come from the more distant feeding place are dancing in quite a different manner. They perform what I have called a

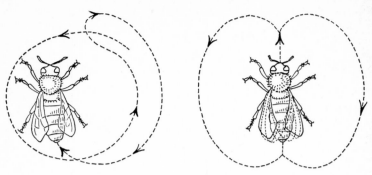

Figure 42. Round dance (*left*) and tail-wagging dance (*right*).

"wagging dance." They run a short distance in a straight line while wagging the abdomen very rapidly from side to side; then they make a complete 360-degree turn to the left, run straight ahead once more, turn to the right, and repeat this pattern over and over again (Figure 42, right). This wagging dance was one that I had observed many years before; but I had always taken it for the characteristic dance of bees bringing pollen to the hive, whereas now I saw that it was performed most vigorously by bees which were bringing in sugar solutions from the experimental feeding place at 300 meters.

It soon became clear that my original interpretation had been incorrect. The error arose because I had always furnished sugar-water at feeding sites close to the hive, chiefly for convenience of observation. The pollen carriers, on the other hand, were arriving from their natural feeding places on flowers some distance away. (Bees carrying pollen can easily be distinguished in the observation hive by the tightly packed pollen baskets formed by stiff hairs attached to the hind legs.) Hence I had seen round dances performed only by bees which were gathering nectar or sugar-water, and wagging dances only by pollen carriers. But once I realized that the two types of dances were related to the *distance* of the food source and not to the nature of the food, it was easy to show by suitable experiments that the dances of pollen gatherers are no different from those performed by nectar gatherers returning from the same distance.

It seems as though a happy dispensation from my scientific guiding star allowed me to discover this error myself. But let younger investigators be warned by this example, as they strive impatiently to publish their results after long years of frustration. Let them test their findings doubly and trebly before they regard any interpretation as certain. For often nature reaches her goal by another path, where man cannot see his way.

I also modified the experiments described above by gradually moving the nearer feeding place from 10 meters to greater and greater distances; as I did this, the same group of numbered bees continued to return to the dish. But between 50 and 100 meters the round dances gave way to wagging dances. At the same time I moved the more distant feeding vessels nearer and nearer to the hive; and as I did so, the same group of bees continued to collect from it. Between 100 meters and 50 meters the wagging dances of this group changed to round dances. It was clear that the round dance and the wagging dance are two different terms in the language of bees, the former meaning a source of food near the hive and the latter a source at 100 meters or more (von Frisch, 1946a,b).

The dances are apparently understood by the bees in the hive, as could be shown by the following experiment. One group of numbered bees was induced to gather food at a feeding place 10 meters from the hive, while another group was fed at a second site 200 meters away. At both locations the feeding vessels were situated on unscented cards. We then stopped supplying sugar at both places, and allowed the dishes to remain empty for an hour or two. After this time most of the bees from both groups were sitting inactive in the hive; only from time to time would one of them fly out to the feeding place to see if anything was to be had. If we now refilled the dish at the more distant site, then the wagging dances of the first gatherers to return with full stomachs aroused chiefly bees from the group which had previously visited the distant feeding place. But when we offered sugar-water at the nearer site, then the resulting round dances aroused mostly bees which had previously been feeding there.

When bees are actively collecting food from flowers they often fly out to a distance of a mile or more from their hive. Under these circumstances a message telling only that a food source was nearer or farther than 100 meters could scarcely have much biological value. As a matter of fact, the wagging dance not only announces that there is a rich source that is far away; it also tells *how* far away. The distance is indicated in a rather exact manner by the number of turns in the wagging dance that are made in a given time. By gradually moving a feeding

site to greater and greater distances we reached 6 kilometers (3.7 miles), after rather strenuous and exciting
experiments. We counted the number of turns per unit
time made by dancers returning from distances ranging
from 100 meters up to 6 kilometers. Figure 43 shows the

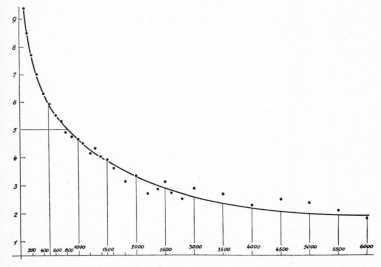

Figure 43. The distance of the feeding place is indicated by the
number of turns of the wagging dance within a given time. *Abscissa:*
The distance of the feeding place in meters. *Ordinate:* The number
of turns within 15 seconds. The curve is the result of 3,885 observed
dances of bees collecting food at distances from 100 to 6,000 meters.

result of 3,885 such observations. At 100 meters there
were 9 to 10 complete cycles of the dance within 15
seconds; at 200 meters there were 7; at 1 kilometer, 4½;
and at 6 kilometers, only 2. If we know this relation between rate of turning and distance to the food, we can tell
by means of a stop watch about how far a dancing bee

has flown. The bees in the hive can also understand the meaning of the dancer's rate of turning and can perceive the distance they must fly to reach the food.

In Figure 43 the individual points (each of which represents the average of many observations) do not all lie precisely upon the curve that relates the rate of turning to the distance of the food. There seem to be three chief reasons for this variability. First, there is some individual variability from one bee to the next; but it is surprising how small this is under ordinary circumstances. Second, there is a definite rate for any distance which is characteristic of a particular colony of bees; that is, the curves relating the rate of turning to the distance of the food often vary from one colony to another. And, third, the rate varies with the direction of the wind. A head wind on the way to the feeding place has the same effect as increased distance; it slows the dances. A tail wind has the opposite effect. The time or the effort needed to reach the food seems to be the basis for the bee's estimation of distance (von Frisch, 1948b).

When the feeding place is near the hive, bees which have been aroused by the round dances fly out in all directions and seek for food in the immediate vicinity. If the source is farther away, the bees learn from the wagging dance, as we have seen, the distance at which the newly discovered food lies. But in addition they learn the *direction* in which they must fly. This surprising fact can be demonstrated by experiments of the following type: We feed some numbered bees on a scented card situated 200 meters south of the hive. Other cards, bearing the same scent but without food, are set out on all sides of the beehive at a distance of 200 meters. Within a few minutes many new bees appear, not only at the feeding place but at the other cards lying nearby. But at the cards lying in other directions we do not see a single bee, or at most a very few. If we shift the food to one of the other directions, say, to the card 200 meters *east* of the hive, we find after a short time that newly aroused bees fly out to the east. The language of bees is truly perfect, and their method of indicating the direction of food sources is one of the most remarkable mysteries of their complex social organization.

If we observe dancers which have returned from a feeding place whose location is known to us, it is surprising to see that all these bees perform the same dance; in particular, they always head in the same direction during the straight part of the wagging dance (see Figure 42). In a typical case the bees collecting at a food source 200 meters south of the hive danced on the honeycombs in such a way that the straight portion of their dance was always headed to the left. If at the same time other bees were gathering sugar-water from a feeding place 200 meters north of the hive, we saw that they pointed to the right during the straight phase of the dance. In other words, the direction of the straight part of the wagging dance is related in some way to the direction of the food source.

When we watched the dances over a period of several hours, always supplying sugar at the same feeding place, we saw that the direction of the straight part of the dances was not constant, but gradually shifted so that it was always quite different in the afternoon from what it had been in the morning. More detailed observations showed that the direction of the dances always changed by approximately the same angle as the earth's rotation and the apparent motion of the sun across the sky. This was not entirely unexpected, since experiments carried out several years before by Wolf, Santschi, and others had shown that both bees and ants often use the sun as a sort of compass when traveling over a level plain without striking landmarks. These earlier observations had involved bees or ants which went out from their homes in search of food and then returned before the direction of the sun had changed appreciably. If a worker bee has flown toward the sun in leaving the hive, she has only to fly directly away from the sun to find her way home. If the sun is to her right on the trip away from the hive, the bee keeps it on her left during the flight home. Hence, when we found that the straight part of the wagging dance shifted with the sun's position, it became clear that these dances also indicated the direction of the feeding place with reference to the sun.

The key to an understanding of this message is a very curious one. We must recall that under normal circumstances a bee dances on the perpendicular honeycomb inside a hive where it is quite dark. In the ordinary hive bees cannot perceive the direction of the sun, but apparently rely instead on the direction of gravity. They orient the straight portion of the dance at the same angle to the force of gravity as the angle they have flown with respect to the sun during the flight from hive to feeding place (Figure 44). If a dancer heads directly upward during the straight part of her dance on the honeycomb,

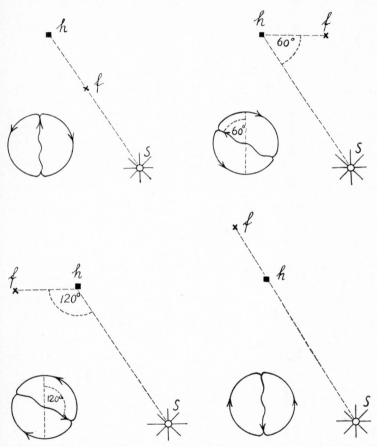

Figure 44. h = beehive, f = feeding place, s = sun's position. At left of each diagram is shown how the bees dance on the perpendicular comb to indicate the direction of the feeding place with respect to the sun's position. Note that the bearing of the sun is transferred to the upward direction, perceived by means of gravity.

this apparently means "The feeding place is in the same direction as the sun." If the straight run points down, it means "Fly away from the sun to reach the food." If during the straight portion of the dance the bee heads 60 degrees to the left of vertical, then the feeding place is situated 60 degrees to the left of the sun. Similarly, a dance with its straight run pointed 120 degrees to the right of vertical indicates a feeding place situated 120 degrees to the right of the sun's position in the sky (von Frisch, 1946a,b, 1948b).

It is remarkable that the heading *toward the sun* is the direction of flight selected to correspond with an *upward* movement during the straight component of the wagging dance. One cannot believe that bees decided all at once to arrange matters thus. We may be sure that this meaningful relationship has developed gradually, like other abilities, in the course of the history of the species. It would be of great interest to investigate more primitive social insects to learn whether they have a simpler kind of language which would show us how the complex situation found in honeybees may have been developed.

Even if the sky is cloudy, bees still indicate by means of the wagging dance the correct direction to the feeding place with reference to the sun's position. Hence they must know where the sun stands in the sky even when it is hidden behind a cloud. Do they perhaps know from experience where the sun will be at a given time of day? Bees have a very good memory for time. If one feeds them at a certain spot for a few days between ten and twelve o'clock, they visit this spot for the next few days from ten to twelve even though the food dish is empty. Hence it seemed to be a real possibility that in territory which was known to them my bees might have been aware of the direction in which the sun stood at each hour of the day. To test this supposition we carried the observation hive far away into territory which was quite unknown to the bees, and we selected for this experiment a morning when the sky was covered with solid clouds. In this new location we set out a feeding place and moved it gradually to a distance of 100 meters from the hive. Even under these conditions the wagging dances indicated correctly the position of the feeding place with reference to the sun. Yet the bees could not have known from experience where the sun was located at a given time in this unfamiliar territory. Apparently they were able to perceive the sun's position directly, despite the cloud cover, but we do not know at present how they can do this.

The bees which are aroused by the dances on the honeycombs recognize the angle of the dance relative to gravity, and in flying out to the food they remember this angle and relate it to the position of the sun. We performed a few experiments to see how precisely the bees hold to the direction indicated by the dancers in the hive. The result of one such study is reproduced in Figure 45. The feeding place lay 250 meters south of the hive; at this point a few numbered bees were fed at a card scented with lavender oil. At 200 meters from the hive seven other cards were set upon the ground, each provided with the same scent but without food. One was

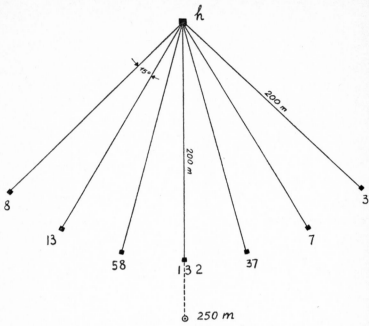

Figure 45. At a feeding place 250 meters south of the beehive (*h*), several numbered bees were fed on a cardboard provided with lavender oil. Somewhat nearer to the hive were placed seven cards provided with the same scent but without food. The number of bees visiting each card within 1 hour can be seen from the drawing. It is remarkable how closely the newcomers keep to the direction indicated by the dancers.

on a direct line between the hive and the feeding place, three lay to the right, and three to the left at 15-degree intervals. We counted all the bees that visited each of these cards during one hour while food was being supplied at the feeding place; the numbers of bees coming to the various cards were (from left to right): 8, 13, 58, 132, 37, 7, and 3. In other words, the great majority

(88 per cent) of bees did not deviate more than 15 degrees from the correct direction.[1]

Another experiment demonstrated the different responses that follow the round dance and the wagging dance. We first set out a scented feeding place 10 meters east of the observation hive. Then cards with the same scent but without food were placed on the ground 25 meters from the hive, one in the same direction and others to the north, west, and south (Figure 46). The numbered

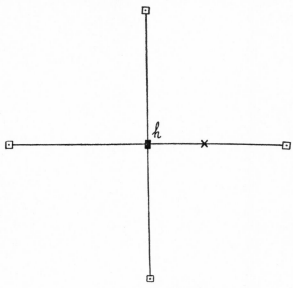

Figure 46. h = beehive, x = feeding place 10 meters east of the hive. The four squares indicate the position of cards provided with the same scent as the feeding place, but without food. See Figure 47.

[1] The experiment was repeated on September 27, 1949, with another stock of bees and in a different locality. The result was even better; the number of visitors was, from left to right, 0, 3, 8, 24, 2, 3, 0.

bees returning from the nearer feeding place performed round dances as usual; within one hour we had counted the following numbers of bees at the four scented cards lying 25 meters from the hive: to the east, 27 bees, and in the other directions, 37, 20, and 19 bees respectively (Figure 47, left). Thus the round dances did not indicate

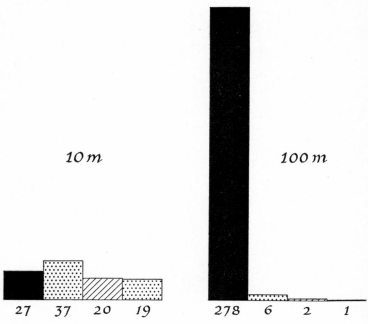

Figure 47. Bees collecting food at a distance of 10 meters perform round dances and thus send out other bees in about equal numbers in all directions (*left*). Bees collecting food at a distance of 100 meters perform tail-wagging dances and send out the other bees in the correct direction (*right*). The heights of the columns show the number of visitors at the 4 cards (see Figure 46), the black column indicating the card in the direction of the feeding place, the column with oblique lines indicating the card in the opposite direction, and the dotted columns indicating the cards situated at right angles to the direction to the feeding place. The exact number of visitors is given by the figures below the columns.

direction to any significant degree; the bees sought for food on all sides of the hive. Later, the same feeding vessel was moved to a point 100 meters north of the hive and the experiment was repeated. Within one hour we now counted 278 bees visiting scented cards north of the hive, and only 6, 2, and 1 at three other cards lying 100 meters to the east, south, and west (Figure 47, right). The bees returning from 100 meters performed wagging dances that conveyed a clear message about the direction in which food was to be found.

In the mountains of my native country the terrain itself suggested the experiment of setting the feeding place behind a ridge, so that the bees would be obliged to fly a detour in order to reach it (Figure 48). I was very curious

Figure 48. To reach the feeding place (*f*), the bees coming from the hive (*h*) have to fly around the corner of a steep hill. The hill is shown in contour.

to see whether they would indicate the direction of the first or the second portion of the route. But the dancing bees actually indicated neither the first nor the second direction, but the "bee line" straight from hive to food. On one occasion I found a location on a certain mountain which was especially suitable for experiments in which the bees were obliged to reach the food by an extensive detour. The observation hive was on one side of a steep ridge and the feeding place was on the other side (Figure 49). We gradually moved the feeding vessel around

Figure 49. Another experiment in which the bees had to fly a detour. The feeding place is on the left side of the picture (white cross), and the hive is about at the same level on the other side, behind the ridge.

the ridge while a group of bees continued to gather sugar-water from it. But the result was a disappointment, for the bees surprised us by flying up and over the ridge.

They had apparently discovered very quickly that the flight path over the rock was a little shorter than the detour around the end of the ridge. They did not deviate from the compass direction, but the actual distance of their flight was much greater than a straight line drawn through the ridge from hive to feeding place. By timing the dances in the observation hive we could see that they were indicating the distance of the actual flight over the ridge rather than the straight-line distance. It is doubtless advantageous in such a situation that the new bees are told not only the absolute direction, but the actual distance of flight along the most feasible route. But even though I have seen this happen, I am unable to comprehend this ability of the bees (von Frisch, 1948b).

Twenty-five years ago I thought I understood the language of bees. But further experiments brought many surprises, one of which was the discovery that the round and the wagging dances conveyed information about the distance of the food source rather than about the kind of food. It was another revelation to find that the wagging dance also told the direction of the food source relative to the sun. But the greatest surprise of all has come to light even more recently.

At one time the outcome of my experiments seemed too fantastic for belief. I wondered whether perhaps the bees of my observation hive had developed into a sort of scientific bee. I decided to see whether the same dances would occur in an ordinary hive. This was clearly so, for I could lift one honeycomb from a typical hive and see the same type of dances still going on, despite the dis-

Figure 51. The observation hive enclosed in the opaque chamber. On the bench is the entrance for the bees.

normal behavior of a colony of honeybees. Dancing bees can often be seen in warm weather on the horizontal board just in front of the entrance to a hive, when some foraging bees stop at the entrance and deliver nectar to other bees that are waiting outside. In this case they dance in daylight and indicate the direction straight toward the feeding place. Inside the dark hive there is no need for such orientation without reference to gravity because there are ordinarily no horizontal surfaces suitable for dancing.

But from the point of view of the physiologist a question arises: How is it possible for bees to indicate the direction of the feeding place if they are dancing on a horizontal surface and if they cannot see the sun?

I have mentioned that when the observation hive was enclosed in a hut with opaque walls the bees could no longer indicate the direction on horizontal surfaces. My next experiment was to remove one wall of this hut and allow the bees to see only an area of blue sky at some distance from the position of the sun. When the blue sky became visible in this way the dances were instantly put in order; the bees once more pointed directly toward the food. To achieve this result it was enough to provide a crack in the wall which was only 4 inches in width. Indeed, the bees could indicate the correct direction even when we allowed them to see the sky only through a tube 16 inches long and 6 inches in diameter (Figure 52).

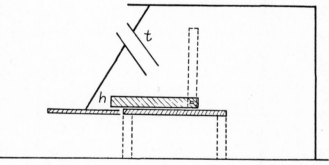

Figure 52. Cross section through the chamber, showing the beehive (*h*) in a horizontal position (normal position indicated by dotted lines). From the location of the dancing bees a spot of blue sky can be seen through the tube (*t*).

If we closed the tube, the dances were disoriented; if we opened it again, they were correct.

In these experiments the tube was pointed upward toward the north sky. The straight part of the dances was directed toward a feeding place to the west. I next placed a mirror just outside of the tube, so that the bees still saw a blue spot, but this was now a reflected image of the sky to the south. Under the influence of the mirror the direction of the dances shifted; the bees pointed east instead of west. From this experiment it was clear that bees can perceive in the sky some phenomenon dependent on the sun's position even though they cannot see the sun directly. As soon as they have recognized the position of the sun they can indicate the direction to the feeding place, keeping the same angle to the sun as they would keep if they were outside the hive and flying to the source of food.

Sometimes a cloud would pass across the area of sky visible through the tube; when this happened the dances became disoriented, and the bees were unable to indicate the direction to the feeding place. Whatever phenomenon in the blue sky served to orient the dances, this experiment showed that it was seriously disturbed if the blue sky was covered by a cloud. We know of such a phenomenon, which is visible in the blue sky, which is related to the position of the sun, and whose intensity is greatly reduced by clouds. It is the polarization of light (von Frisch, 1948b).

Light rays coming directly from the sun consist of vibrations that occur in all directions perpendicular to the line along which the sunlight travels. But the light of the blue sky has not reached us directly from the sun; it has first been scattered from particles in the atmosphere. This diffuse, scattered light coming from the sky is partially polarized, by which we mean that more of it is vibrating in one direction than in others. Devices such as a Nicol prism or a piece of polaroid transmit only the light vibrating in one direction; for this reason they are sometimes called analyzers of polarized light. Hence if one holds such a device before one's eyes while looking at the blue sky, the sky will appear darker or lighter as the analyzer is rotated. It is easy to see by simple inspection of the blue sky through a piece of polaroid that the intensity of polarization varies with the distance from the sun. If one looks at the sky 90 degrees away from the sun, one sees the greatest change in brightness as the analyzer is rotated; as much as 70 per cent of the light may be polarized; but nearer to the sun and farther away from it the degree of polarization diminishes, and it becomes very feeble or absent altogether in the region close to the sun and around the point just opposite.

There is also another relationship between the position of the sun and the polarization of the blue light from the sky. The plane of polarization of the light from any point in the sky is always perpendicular to a second plane determined by three points: the eye of the observer, the spot of sky at which he looks, and the sun. This rule fails to hold only in the neighborhood of the sun and close to the point of sky just opposite to it.[2]

---

[2] These geometrical relations result from the manner in which light is scattered by particles in the atmosphere; a detailed explanation of the whole matter can be found in any standard textbook of optics.

Theoretically at least it is thus possible to determine the sun's position from inspection of an area of blue sky, provided one can detect the polarization of the light with some sort of analyzer.

But such a theoretical possibility could lead to nothing more than speculation until we had learned whether the dances of bees were influenced in any way by changing the polarization of the light coming to them from the blue sky. Such a test was made by using a sheet of polaroid, like the visors that are sometimes attached to automobile windshields for protection against glare. I used a sheet about 6 inches wide and 12 inches long, and every part of the surface of the sheet acted as an analyzer; the light passing through it became polarized in one direction. I placed this sheet over the glass window of my observation hive while the latter lay in a horizontal position, and it became clear at once that the dances were markedly affected. To simplify the experimental situation I placed opaque screens on three sides of the hive; and there was also a roof to exclude light from above. The dancing bees could see the blue sky in only one direction. I observed the dances while varying the position of the polaroid sheet as it lay directly against the glass window.

In 62 series of experiments of this type, performed during the summer of 1948, I found that the following rules seemed to govern the responses of the bees. If the position of the polaroid sheet was such that the plane of vibration of the sky light was not changed appreciably in passing through it, then the dancing bees indicated the direction to the feeding place quite correctly (Figure 53, upper). If

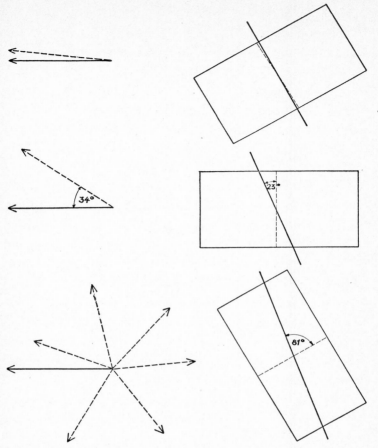

Figure 53. The results of three experiments with the polaroid sheet.
Right: The position of the sheet in each experiment; a solid line shows the plane of vibration of the polarized light coming from the visible area of blue sky; the dotted line shows the plane of vibration after passing the sheet. *Left:* The solid line shows the direction to the feeding place, and the dotted lines, the direction indicated by the dancers under the polaroid sheet (average of about ten dances). *Upper:* The plane of vibration of the polarized light from the blue sky is not significantly changed in passing the sheet; the dances are correct. *Center:* The plane of vibration of the polarized light coming from the blue sky is turned to the right in passing the screen; the dances deviate to the right also. *Lower:* The plane of vibration of the polarized light is turned through 81 degrees; the dances are disoriented.

I turned the sheet like a turntable so that the plane of vibration of the polarized light was shifted, the dances deviated in the same direction (Figure 53, center). If I turned the sheet in the opposite direction, the dances followed the direction of turning. If I turned the sheet through an angle of about 55 degrees or more, then the dances became quite disoriented, as in darkness (Figure 53, lower).

If the plane of polarization of the sky light is really the factor that governs the orientation of the dances, we should obtain the same result by turning the polaroid, as described above, or by changing the direction in which the bees were allowed to see the sky. To test this possibility I modified the experiment as follows. I shifted the position of the opaque screen instead of changing the position of the polaroid sheet. In a typical case the bees had been able to see the sky to the north, and after I turned the opaque screen through 90 degrees they could see the sky only to the west. After this change we could see that the dances had shifted in conformity with the difference in the plane of vibration of the light from the two areas of sky.

The direction of the dances also changes if we alter none of the experimental arrangements but merely wait for the time of day to change. Even though the positions of the polaroid sheet and the opaque screen are both unaltered, the effect of placing the polaroid over the hive is quite different in the morning from what it is in the afternoon. This too conforms with the dependence of the plane of polarization of sky light on the sun's position.

To be sure, there were some deviations from these rules when the east sky was used in the morning, south sky at midday, or west sky in the afternoon, but these probably resulted from the weakness and variability of the polarization in the sky close to the sun. Further experiments with better equipment will be necessary in order to obtain quantitative results.[3] But one fact seems quite clear already: the polarization of the sky light is very important for the orientation of bees (von Frisch, 1949a).

I believe that the importance of polarized light is not limited to bees. Under certain circumstances ants use the sun as a sort of compass. Many years ago Santschi discovered that ants can keep themselves oriented and maintain a steady direction of walking even when surrounded by a screen so that they can see only a piece of blue sky. He suggested that they must be able to see the stars even in daylight. I believe that if we should repeat Santschi's experiment using a piece of polaroid his theory would have to be discarded and another one, no less romantic, put in its place.[4]

The compound eye of an insect (Figure 54) is fixed on the head and seems to be especially suitable for recognizing the polarization over the whole sky at once, provided that we assume that it can act as an analyzer of polarized light—like a Nicol prism or a piece of polaroid. But we do not know yet whether or not this is actually the case.

---

[3] See Appendix.

[4] During the summer of 1949 my student, Miss Schifferer, proved, in some observations not yet published, that ants (*Lasius niger*) also orient themselves by means of the polarization of the sky light.

Thus we see, after traveling a long way, that we have not reached the end of the road, but stand instead at the threshold of new problems.

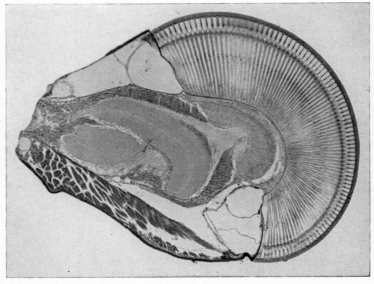

Figure 54. Microphotograph of a section through one eye of an insect (dragonfly), showing the large number of single eyes fixed on the head in such a way that the whole sky always can be observed.

Appendix

SINCE these lectures were given, the summer of 1949 has provided the opportunity to continue our investigations. Some of the results are presented here because they add significantly to our understanding of the nature of the bees' orientation by polarized sky light.

The question of primary concern to us was this: where is the analyzer of polarized light located in the eye of the bee? In Figure 54 is shown a cross section through the entire compound eye. A single facet, or ommatidium, from such a compound eye is shown schematically, and at great magnification, in Figure 55. Each ommatidium admits only the pencil of light which arrives approximately along its own axis. Neighboring ommatidia, with their axes slightly divergent, point in somewhat different directions. Thus the eight to ten thousand ommatidia of the two compound eyes furnish an equal number of points of light, from which the whole field of vision takes shape after the fashion of a mosaic.

The crystalline cone, Cr, has the function of conducting to the photosensitive cells the pencil of rays which

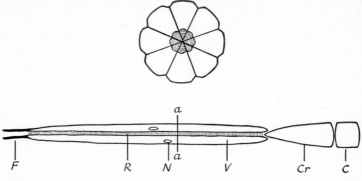

Figure 55. Schematic diagram of a single ommatidium from the compound eye of an insect. C = cornea; Cr = crystalline cone; V = visual cell; N = nucleus of visual cell; R = rhabdome; F = nerve fiber. At the top is a cross section at *aa*, greatly enlarged.

arrives along the axis of the ommatidium. My first conjecture, that this crystalline cone might be the analyzer, was not confirmed by our investigations. In the ommatidium of the bee eight visual cells are attached to the inner end of the crystalline cone, and in cross section these show a radial arrangement (Figure 55, above). Their inner parts (shown as dark areas) form the visual rods or rhabdom, R, in which the light arouses nervous excitation. Each visual cell is supplied by a nerve fiber. My colleague H. Autrum in Göttingen expressed in a letter to me the idea that these radially arranged visual cells could polarize light in different planes, in accordance with their position. If this assumption is correct, even a single ommatidium could theoretically recognize the direction of vibration of the polarized light from any portion of the sky. As was explained earlier, when *we* wish to make such an analysis we must look at the sky through a sheet of polaroid and rotate the sheet. If the radially arranged visual cells function like polaroid, the *bees* would receive simultaneously the different impressions which we obtain one after another as we rotate the analyzer before our eyes.

I next prepared a model which reproduced on a greatly enlarged scale these hypothetical properties of the bee's ommatidium with respect to polarization optics. From a sheet of polaroid [1] I cut out eight isosceles triangles, as indicated in Figure 56. In each triangle the direction of

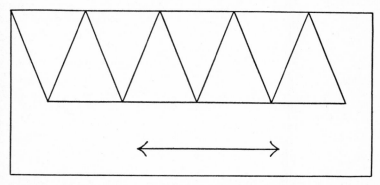

Figure 56. Pattern for cutting triangles from a polaroid sheet to construct a model of the insect ommatidium. The double arrow shows the direction of vibration of the light transmitted by the sheet.

vibration of the transmitted light (shown by the double arrow in the figure) was parallel to the base. These triangles were attached to a glass plate in a radial arrangement (Figure 57), corresponding to the position

[1] I am deeply indebted to Dr. E. H. Land, president of the Polaroid Corporation, for providing us with an ample supply of polaroid material for these experiments.

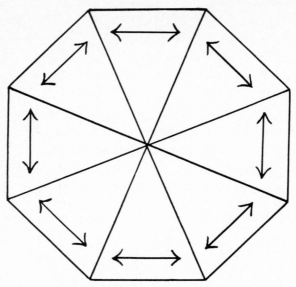

Figure 57. The artificial bee eye constructed from eight triangles of polaroid. The double arrow in each triangle gives the direction of vibration of the transmitted light.

of the visual cells in the ommatidium. This star-shaped pattern of polaroid triangles was mounted so that it could easily be turned to face in any direction, or tilted to any desired angle (Figure 58).

On looking through this instrument at the blue sky, one sees a brightness pattern like that reproduced in photograph 1 of Figure 59. It is easy to understand how this pattern comes about. The sky light toward which the instrument is pointed vibrates predominantly in the plane indicated by the double arrow. This corresponds to the direction of vibration which can pass through the

Figure 58. The artificial eye mounted for observation. The round disk on the table is a sheet of polaroid which can be placed on the side of the artificial eye pointed toward the sky, and rotated to any desired position.

triangles marked "A." These, therefore, appear bright. The triangles marked "C" are arranged perpendicular to those marked "A"; they impede the transmission of the polarized sky light and hence remain dark. The more strongly the incident sky light is polarized, the sharper the contrast between the triangles. The triangles "B" and "D" show an intermediate brightness because they transmit only a component of the polarized light.

When one looks at different portions of the sky through this "artificial bee eye" the pattern is altered,

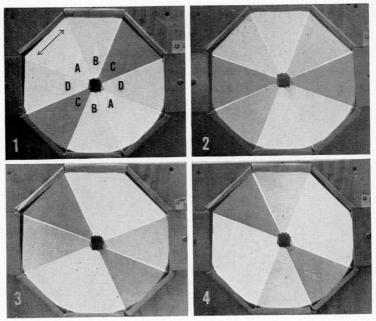

Figure 59. Photograph of blue sky through the artificial eye, 10 A.M., September 25, 1949. Instrument pointed in No. 1 to the west, in No. 2 to the northwest, in No. 3 to the north, and in No. 4 to the northeast.

because the direction of vibration of the polarized light is different. A typical example is shown in Figure 59, photographs 1 to 4. The blue sky was photographed through the instrument at 10 A.M. on September 25, 1949, at 45 degrees above the horizon, in four different directions—west, northwest, north, and northeast. It is clear that each direction gave rise to a typical pattern which did not appear, at this hour, at any other position in the sky. The pattern naturally shifts with the time of day, since it is dependent upon the position of the sun.

If we assume that such brightness patterns also exist in the eyes of bees, and are perceived in any way at all,[2] then these insects would be capable of using each speck of blue sky as a sun compass. They need only maintain a body position allowing the brightness pattern to remain constant in each ommatidium. In our special case of flight from hive to feeding place, each ommatidium sees a characteristic pattern in the minute area of sky at which it is pointed. If the bees dancing on a horizontal comb see a piece of blue sky, they assume, during the straight portion of their dance, that position in which the pattern perceived by one area of their visual field matches the pattern remembered from flights out to the feeding place. In this way they indicate the direction in which food is to be found.

In order to test whether this hypothesis would explain the observed facts, I performed parallel experiments with dancing bees and with the artificial eye. I should like to describe the nature of these experiments and their results by means of four examples.

(1) Let us consider first a group of bees which are dancing in a horizontal observation hive and which have a clear view of one limited area of blue sky. Let us lay

---

[2] One need not assume that the bee sees several thousand little star-shaped patterns. The individual excitations could be centrally integrated to a unified total sensation, just as with us the images furnished by the two eyes are fused into a unified space perception. Naturally we cannot know what visual sensations are actually experienced by a bee.

over the glass window of the hive a sheet of polaroid so oriented that the light from this area of sky passes through the sheet without appreciable change in its direction of vibration. Under these conditions the bees still indicate correctly the direction toward the feeding place. This we had shown in 1948, and the observation was confirmed in 1949 by fourteen additional experiments of this kind. If, during such an experiment, one looks through the artificial eye at the area of sky which is visible to the bees, a characteristic brightness pattern is seen. If one places in front of the instrument a sheet of polaroid oriented just like the sheet lying over the bee-hive—so that the direction of vibration of the polarized sky light is unaltered—then one sees no change in the brightness pattern of the sky visible through the instrument. The pattern merely shows greater contrast, because the light in passing through the polaroid becomes completely polarized, whereas the original sky light was only partially so. In this situation, according to our hypothesis, the actual compound eye of a bee will also see the same pattern with and without the polaroid. Therefore the direction of the dances will not be altered.

(2) On September 5, 1949, I allowed bees in a horizontal observation hive to see a small area of blue sky to the west. The feeding place lay in the same direction, 200 meters from the hive. As in the first experiment, the bees danced correctly when I laid the polaroid over the hive so that the direction of vibration of the incident sky light was not altered; they still pointed to the west. Next I turned the sheet 30 degrees counterclockwise; and

the dances turned in the same direction, but shifted from west to 35 degrees south of west (average of 10 observations). I pointed the artificial eye toward the portion of the western sky which was visible to the dancing bees, and saw the brightness pattern reproduced in the left-hand photograph of Figure 60. Next I placed a sheet of polaroid in front of the instrument, in the same orientation as that lying over the observation hive. The brightness pattern shifted to that shown in the center photograph of Figure 60. If I now removed the sheet of polaroid and turned the artificial eye toward other directions, I found this same pattern at 34 degrees north of west (right-hand photograph of Figure 60). This

Figure 60. Photograph of blue sky through the artificial eye at 9:40–10:00 A.M., September 5, 1949. *Left:* West sky as seen through the instrument. *Center:* Same, with polaroid placed over the instrument in the same orientation as the polaroid placed over the observation hive. *Right:* The same pattern is to be seen through the instrument, *without* the polaroid sheet, at 34 degrees north of west.

pattern was not to be observed in any other direction.

From these results it became clear why the bees had turned south by a slightly greater angle than the 30 degrees through which the polaroid was rotated. During flight from hive to feeding place they had seen the left-hand pattern of Figure 60 directly ahead and to the west. But 34 degrees to the right they had seen the pattern shown in the center and right-hand photographs of Figure 60. When the polaroid sheet was rotated through 30 degrees before the window of the observation hive, the center pattern of Figure 60 was thereby presented to the bees as the only visible area of polarized light. These relationships are diagramed in Figure 61, where the original pattern visible straight ahead, to the west, is designated No. 1, while the pattern visible out of doors at 34 degrees north of west is called No. 2. In our experiment we first presented pattern No. 1, and the bees pointed directly toward it; but on applying the polaroid we offered, in the same window, pattern No. 2. The second pattern was that which the bees had seen at 34 degrees to their right as they had flown out from the hive to the feeding place, and hence they now pointed their dances 35 degrees to the left of the position where this pattern was presented. Thus they indicated a direction which deviated 35 degrees from the flight line to the feeding place but which conformed within one degree to the direction predicted by our hypothesis.

I had found in similar experiments during 1948 that when the polaroid sheet was rotated, the dances shifted in the same direction. However, I had been unable to understand why the direction of the dances sometimes shifted through the same angle as that by which the polaroid was turned, and yet at other times shifted through some quite different angle. By control experiments with the artificial eye we showed that the direction of the dances always shifted by the same angle as that to which the brightness pattern in the sky was displaced

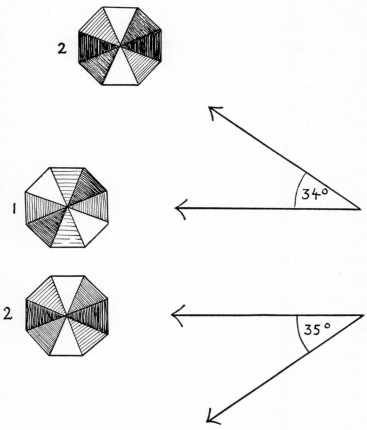

Figure 61. Upper: The bees see straight ahead of them (to the west), when flying from hive to feeding place, pattern No. 1; they also see pattern No. 2 at 34 degrees to the right. *Lower:* In the experiment the dancing bees saw pattern No. 2 as they looked out from the window of the observation hive; hence they indicated by their dances that the feeding place lay 35 degrees to the left of the window.

under the particular conditions of the experiment. In 48 such experiments the difference between the observed direction of the dances and that predicted by this theory averaged 8 degrees, with a maximum difference of 20 degrees. This is a good agreement, when one considers the sources of error which enter into these experiments.

(3) Out of a total of 83 experiments of this kind during the summer of 1949, there were 16 in which the bees did not point in any definite direction when the polaroid was in place, but rather danced in an entirely disoriented fashion. Simultaneous observations with the artificial eye showed that in these cases—and *only* in these cases—the pattern which was produced by placing a polaroid over the instrument could not, at the time of the experiment, be found in *any part of the sky* when one looked through the instrument without the sheet of polaroid in front of it.

(4) In 4 of the 83 experiments a remarkable phenomenon appeared—the bees pointed in two different directions, one corresponding to a mirror image of the other. Often they shifted by 180 degrees several times during a single dance. In these cases—and *only* in these cases—the pattern produced by placing a polaroid over the artificial eye appeared in the sky at *two* points directly opposite from each other (von Frisch, 1950).

To describe the details of these recent experiments would carry us too far from the original content of the lectures. Yet I wished to show by this brief summary that the ability of bees to orient themselves by the polarization of sky light has been confirmed in a surprising fashion, and that we too can form a conception of the mechanism by which this orientation is achieved. However, our experiments have not conclusively proved that the mechanism in the eye of the bee is the same as that of our model. It is also possible that in the compound eye the analysis of polarized light is accomplished in some other way. But the recent investigations of Autrum (1950), employing an entirely different technique, have made it seem probable that our concept is correct and that the single ommatidium functions as an analyzer of polarized light.

Bibliography

Autrum, H. Über Energie- und Zeitgrenzen der Sinnesempfindungen. Die Naturwissenschaften, *35:* 361–369, 1948.

——. Neue Versuche zum optischen Auflösungsvermögen fliegender Insekten. Experientia, *5:* 271–277, 1949.

—— and H. Stumpf. Das Bienenauge als Analysator für polarisiertes Licht. Zeitschrift für Naturforschung, *5b:* 116–122, 1950.

Bauer, L. Geschmacksphysiologische Untersuchungen an Wasserkäfern. Zeitschrift für vergleichende Physiologie, *26:* 107–120, 1939.

Beling, I. Über das Zeitgedächtnis der Bienen. Zeitschrift für vergleichende Physiologie, *9:* 259–338, 1929.

Beutler, R. Biologisch-chemische Untersuchungen am Nektar von Immenblumen. Zeitschrift für vergleichende Physiologie, *12:* 72–176, 1930.

Forel, A. Das Sinnesleben der Insekten. München: Reinhardt, 1910. (English translation: The senses of insects. London: Methuen, 1908.)

Frisch, K. von. Der Farbensinn und Formensinn der Biene. Zoologische Jahrbücher, Abteilung für allgemeine Zoologie und Physiologie, *35:* 1–182, 1915.

——. Über den Geruchsinn der Biene und seine blütenbiologische Bedeutung. Zoologische Jahrbücher, Abteilung für allgemeine Zoologie und Physiologie, *37:* 1–238, 1919.

Frisch, K. von. Über den Sitz des Geruchsinnes bei Insekten. Zoologische Jahrbücher, Abteilung für allgemeine Zoologie und Physiologie, *38:* 1–68, 1921.

———. Das Problem des tierischen Farbensinnes. Die Naturwissenschaften, *11:* 470–476, 1923a.

———. Über die "Sprache" der Bienen. Zoologische Jahrbücher, Abteilung für allgemeine Zoologie und Physiologie, *40:* 1–186, 1923b.

———. Ein Vorschlag für die Wanderimker. Bienenzucht und Bienenforschung in Bayern (Wacholtz-Verlag, Neumünster), pp. 1–4, 1927.

———. Über den Geschmackssinn der Bienen. Zeitschrift für vergleichende Physiologie, *21:* 1–156, 1934.

———. Christian Konrad Sprengels Blumentheorie vor 150 Jahren und heute. Die Naturwissenschaften, *31:* 223–229, 1943.

———. Die "Sprache" der Bienen und ihre Nutzanwendung in der Landwirtschaft. Experientia, *2:* 397–404, 1946a.

———. Die Tänze der Bienen. Österreichische zoologische Zeitschrift, *1:* 1–48, 1946b.

———. Duftgelenkte Bienen im Dienste der Landwirtschaft und Imkerei. Wien. Springer-Verlag, 1947.

———. Aus dem Leben der Bienen, 4th edition. Wien: Springer-Verlag, 1948a.

———. Gelöste und ungelöste Rätsel der Bienensprache. Die Naturwissenschaften, *35:* 38–43, 1948b.

———. Die Polarisation des Himmelslichtes als orientierender Faktor bei den Tänzen der Bienen. Experientia, *5:* 142–148, 1949a.

——. Du und das Leben. Berlin: Verlag Druckhaus Tempelhof, 1949b.

——. Die Sonne als Kompass im Leben der Bienen. Experientia, *6:* 210–221, 1950.

Haslinger, F. Über den Geschmacksinn von Calliphora erythrocephala und über die Verwertung von Zuckern und Zuckeralkoholen durch diese Fliege. Zeitschrift für vergleichende Physiologie, *22:* 614–640, 1935.

Hertz, M. Die Organisation des optischen Feldes bei der Biene, I, II, and III. Zeitschrift für vergleichende Physiologie, *8:* 693–748, 1929a; *11:* 107–145, 1929b; *14:* 629–674, 1931.

——. Über figurale Intensitäten und Qualitäten in der optischen Wahrnehmung der Biene. Biologisches Zentralblatt, *53:* 10–40, 1933.

——. Die Untersuchungen über den Formensinn der Honigbiene. Die Naturwissenschaften, *23:* 618–624, 1935.

——. Beitrag zum Farbensinn und Formensinn der Biene. Zeitschrift für vergleichende Physiologie, *24:* 413–421, 1937a.

——. Versuche über das Farbensystem der Bienen. Die Naturwissenschaften, *25:* 492–493, 1937b.

——. Zur Technik und Methode der Bienenversuche mit Farbpapieren und Glasfiltern. Zeitschrift für vergleichende Physiologie, *25:* 239–250, 1937c.

——. New experiments on colour vision in bees. Journal of Experimental Biology, *16:* 1–8, 1939.

Hess, C. von. Gesichtssinn. Wintersteins Handbuch der vergleichenden Physiologie, Vol. 4: 555–840. Jena: Fischer, 1913.

Honigmann, H. Untersuchungen über Lichtempfindlichkeit und Adaptierung des Vogelauges. Pflüger's Archiv für die gesamte Physiologie, *189:* 1–72, 1921.

Ilse, D. Über den Farbensinn der Tagfalter. Zeitschrift für vergleichende Physiologie, *8:* 658–692, 1928.

Kleber, E. Hat das Zeitgedächtnis der Bienen biologische Bedeutung? Zeitschrift für vergleichende Physiologie, *22:* 221–262, 1935.

Knoll, F. Insekten und Blumen. Abhandlungen der Zoologisch-Botanischen Gesellschaft in Wien, *12:* 1–377, 1921.

Kühn, A. Über den Farbensinn der Bienen. Zeitschrift für vergleichende Physiologie, *5:* 762–800, 1927.

Lotmar, R. Neue Untersuchungen über den Farbensinn der Bienen, mit besonderer Berücksichtigung des Ultravioletts. Zeitschrift für vergleichende Physiologie, *19:* 673–723, 1933.

Minnich, D. E. The chemical sensitivity of the tarsi of the red admiral butterfly, *Pyrameis atalanta* L. Journal of Experimental Zoology, *35:* 57–81, 1922a.

——. A quantitative study of tarsal sensitivity to solutions of saccharose, in the red admiral butterfly, *Pyrameis atalanta* L. Journal of Experimental Zoology, *36:* 445–457, 1922b.

——. The chemical sensitivity of the legs of the blow-fly, *Calliphora vomitoria* L., to various sugars. Zeitschrift für vergleichende Physiologie, *11:* 1–55, 1929.

——. The contact chemoreceptors of the honey bee, *Apis mellifera* L. Journal of Experimental Zoology, *61:* 375–393, 1932.

Oettingen-Spielberg, T. zu. Über das Wesen der Suchbiene. Zeitschrift für vergleichende Physiologie, *31:* 454–489, 1949.

Park, O. W. Studies on the sugar concentration of the nectar of various plants. Report of the Iowa State Apiarist, 1928: 80–89.

Porsch, O. Grellrot als Vogelblumenfarbe. Biologia generalis (Wien), 7: 647–674, 1931.

Ritter, E. Untersuchungen über den chemischen Sinn beim schwarzen Kolbenwasserkäfer, *Hydrous piceus.* Zeitschrift für vergleichende Physiologie, 23: 543–568, 1936.

Santschi, F. Observations et remarques critiques sur le mécanisme de l'orientation chez les fourmis. Revue Suisse de Zoologie, 19: 303–338, 1911.

——. L'orientation sidérale des fourmis et quelques considérations sur leurs différentes possibilités d'orientation. Mémoires de la Sociéte Vaudoise des Sciences Naturelles, 1: 137–176, 1923.

Schaller, A. Sinnesphysiologische und psychologische Untersuchungen an Wasserkäfern und Fischen. Zeitschrift für vergleichende Physiologie, 4: 370–464, 1926.

Scharrer, E. Die Empfindlichkeit der freien Flossenstrahlen der Knurrhahns (*Trigla*) für chemische Reize. Zeitschrift für vergleichende Physiologie, 22: 145–154, 1935.

Sprengel, C. K. Das entdeckte Geheimnis der Natur im Bau und in der Befruchtung der Blumen (Berlin, 1793). Republished in four volumes edited by Paul Knuth as Nos. 48–51 of Ostwald's Klassiker der exakten Wissenschaften. Leipzig: Engelmann, 1894.

Steinhoff, H. Untersuchungen über die Haftfähigkeit von Duftstoffen am Bienenkörper. Zeitschrift für vergleichende Physiologie, 31: 38–57, 1948.

Thorpe, W. H. Orientation and methods of communication of the honey bee and its sensitivity to the polarization of the light. Nature, 164 (4157): 11–14, 1949.

Vogel, B. Über die Beziehungen zwischen Süssgeschmack

und Nährwert von Zuckern und Zuckeralkoholen bei der Honigbiene. Zeitschrift für vergleichende Physiologie, *14:* 273–347, 1931.

Wahl, O. Neue Untersuchungen über das Zeitgedächtnis der Bienen. Zeitschrift für vergleichende Physiologie, *16:* 529–589, 1932.

——. Beitrag zur Frage der biologischen Bedeutung des Zeitgedächtnisses der Bienen. Zeitschrift für vergleichende Physiologie, *18:* 709–717, 1933.

——. Untersuchungen über ein geeignetes Vergällungsmittel für Bienenzucker. Zeitschrift für vergleichende Physiologie, *24:* 116–142, 1937.

Wolf, E. Über das Heimkehrvermögen der Bienen. Zeitschrift für vergleichende Physiologie, *6:* 221–254, 1927.

Index